Sapphie had ... **strength to fi**...

He took her into his arms, his brilliant blue gaze holding hers briefly before he lowered his head and his mouth claimed hers.

Oh…!

Her need for this man was just too much for her to resist, her lips parting beneath his even as her arms moved up over his shoulders.

Rik deepened the kiss, his arms tightening about her waist as he moulded her slender curves to the harder planes of his body.

Nothing had changed, Sapphie acknowledged achingly; she loved and wanted this man. Only this man. She realised now that she always would.

THE PRINCE BROTHERS

Enter the glamorous world of these gorgeous men…

Enter the glamorous world of the movies when you read about the love lives of the celebrity Prince brothers, owners of the prestigious company PrinceMovies. Each brother is super-successful in his field:

Arrogant, forceful and determined, the oldest, **Nik,** is a movie director.
Enjoy his story in

PRINCE'S PASSION
October 2005

A former bad boy, **Zak** is now a world-famous actor, known for being a charming rogue.
Meet him in

PRINCE'S PLEASURE
November 2005

And the youngest, **Rik,** is a screenwriter who's more reserved than his brothers, but irresistible to women.
You can read about his life in

PRINCE'S LOVE-CHILD
January 2006

PRINCE'S LOVE-CHILD

BY
CAROLE MORTIMER

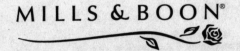

MILLS & BOON®

First published in Great Britain 2005
Paperback Edition 2006
Harlequin Mills & Boon Limited,
Eton House, 18-24 Paradise Road, Richmond, Surrey TW9 1SR

© Carole Mortimer 2005

ISBN 0 263 84782 9

Set in Times Roman 10½ on 12½ pt.
01-0106-43723

Printed and bound in Spain
by Litografia Rosés, S.A., Barcelona

PROLOGUE

'Rik…! Rik Prince, can that really be you…?'

He froze at the first sound of that husky, sensual voice. No—it was worse than that, he actually felt paralysed, every muscle and sinew immobile with shock, his chest having stopped rising and falling, only his heart, with a will of its own, continuing to beat. But faster, so much faster than normal, as if trying to protect itself from the onslaught of remembered pain.

That voice!

So easily recognisable, so painfully remembered. It was the voice that had spoken to him in his dreams so often in the past. The voice that, for months, had motivated him to pick up the telephone a dozen times a day, hoping to hear its honeyed warmth on the other end of the line…

Calls he had never made. But, he realised now, he hadn't thought of her for months; his previous unhappiness was completely buried.

Or so he had thought…

'Rik…?' The precisely English-accented tones were closer now.

In fact, as her hand reached out to touch him gently on his T-shirted back, Rik knew she had to be standing directly behind him.

How the hell was he supposed to deal with seeing her again after all this time?

He wasn't dealing with it at all at this moment; just standing here in the middle of the street, paralysed with shock, couldn't be classed as dealing with anything!

Breathe, you idiot, he instructed himself firmly, relieved when his body obeyed the command and his chest began to rise and fall once again. Now turn around, he ordered determinedly. Just turn around and face her. It couldn't be any harder than walking away from her had been five years ago.

Could it...?

If anything she was more beautiful than ever; tall, golden and tanned, with the most incredible green eyes he had ever seen. Diamond McCall. And how she lived up to that name—her beauty was dazzling.

Even in a skimpy pink T-shirt and ragged denim cut-offs, there was no doubting that this woman was *someone*. In Dee's case, despite or because of her melodious English tones, she was the present highest-paid actress in Hollywood, her name at the top of the credits, and enough to guarantee any movie she was in would be a box-office hit.

She was also someone else's wife...!

'I thought it was you!' she exclaimed excitedly now, her face alight with pleasure as she smiled at him. 'But how marvellous!' she beamed, one long, slender hand reaching out to grasp the strength of his bare forearm. 'I had heard that if you sat outside Fouquet's on the Champs-Elysées for long enough you would eventually see everyone in Paris who was

anyone walking by, but I never believed it until now!'
She gave an amazed shake of her head, long, honey-
coloured hair swaying against her tanned shoulders.
'What on earth are you doing in Paris?'

His mind had gone completely blank. Had been so
since the moment he looked into those deep green
eyes.

Why was he here? In fact, who the hell was he?
Damned if he knew…!

'Rik…?' Dee gave him a quizzical look now. 'You
aren't still angry with me, are you?' she cooed.

Angry with her? Had he ever been angry with her?
Hadn't his anger all been reserved for her manipula-
tive stepmother and stepsister, both so determined that
Dee would marry the mega-rich and powerful Jerome
Powers? As he looked at Dee now, so beautiful, so
intensely alive, it was difficult to believe anyone
could ever be cruel or angry with her.

She gave him a poutingly reproving smile. 'At least
say something, darling!'

He wasn't sure that he could, his tongue seeming
cleaved to the roof of his mouth, like some awkward
schoolboy. Which for a man of thirty-five, with a suc-
cession of screenwriting awards to his credit, plus
ownership of a movie company with his older brothers, Nik and Zak, was pretty pathetic.

It was because he had had no warning of this meeting, he consoled himself.

Today had begun like any other day of his two
months' stay in Paris: he woke at eight o'clock, went
for a brisk walk beside the Seine, returned to his hotel
for a breakfast of coffee and croissants and lingering

over the newspaper, before venturing out again later in search of somewhere to eat lunch.

Nowhere in any of that relaxed routine had he had the least premonition that he would also see Dee McCall again today!

But he had to say something, couldn't stand here like a speechless moron for ever.

'You're looking well, Dee,' he finally managed gruffly, his American accent totally at variance with her softer English tones.

'So are you, Rik,' she returned softly, her eyes flirting with him beneath lowered dark lashes. 'Are you—?'

'Is—?' He broke off as they both began talking at once. 'You first,' he invited wryly.

He might not have thought of this woman for months—years?—but when he had, he had never imagined the two of them meeting like this, awkwardly, stilted, like two strangers who had never been madly in love with each other. He hadn't imagined Cathy and Heathcliffe either, but this—this was just banal!

Dee gave him a mischievous smile. 'I was just going to ask if you're here with someone.'

He shook his head. 'And I was just going to ask if you were here with Jerome.' Her husband. The man she had married five years ago instead of him. Despite all his pleadings for her to do otherwise.

It wasn't a period of his life he was particularly proud of, but at the time he had been so much in love with Dee that nothing else seemed to matter.

At the time...?

Yes, at the time, he realised dazedly now as he looked at her, because he wasn't still in love with Dee; time, and absence, had made that impossible to sustain. It was the memory of what they once had together, those fierce, snatched times together, that had kept her memory so much alive.

She had been so young, only twenty, on the way up in the world of acting, pressurised by her stepmother and stepsister into becoming engaged to and marrying Jerome Powers, then a man of forty and even more powerful in the world of media and entertainment than the three Prince brothers.

Rik had argued, Dee had been stubbornly adamant, tearfully pleading with him to understand that she had to marry Jerome in order to get away from her grasping stepmother and stepsister. His promises that he could—and would—protect her in the same way, had all been tearfully rebuffed.

No, he wasn't still in love with Dee, but the anger he felt towards her stepmother and stepsister was still there!

'Dee-Dee, you have to come and look at the most beautiful little purse and pocketbook we found for you!' a man's deep voice interrupted.

Rik didn't need to turn to know who that man was; only one person called Diamond McCall Dee-Dee in that possessive tone; Jerome Powers, Dee's husband of the last five years.

'Hello, who—Rik…? Rik Prince!' Jerome greeted warmly as Rik finally steeled himself to turn and look at him. 'What on earth are you doing in Paris?'

Jerome smiled at him warmly, at the same time dropping a lightly possessive arm about Dee's shoulders.

It was impossible not to like this man, with his genuine warmth and charm, his iron-grey hair and sophisticated good looks attracting women of all ages. Even Rik couldn't help liking Jerome, and it would have been so much easier to dislike the man who was married to Dee.

'I was working for a while,' Rik answered, 'but now I'm just taking a couple of days' holiday before returning to the States.'

Jerome nodded. 'How are Nik and Zak? I heard they both got married recently. Making you the last of the Eligible Princes, I guess.' He grinned good-humouredly.

A grin Rik found very hard to return; if things had worked out for him five years ago he would have been the first of the Prince brothers to marry. Except the woman he had loved had married this guy instead...

'They're both good,' Rik nodded. 'Very happy, in fact.' Yet another reason for him to spend this time in Paris. Not that he begrudged his older brothers their newfound happiness, because he didn't, knew both of them were married to lovely women. But the settled happiness of his siblings made his own bachelor state seem all the more lonely.

Meeting Dee again like this in the company of her husband wasn't helping that situation.

'Excellent.' Jerome nodded happily. 'Dee-Dee, would you like to come and look in the store? I just know you're going to love the purse and pocketbook, and—hell, where are my manners?' Jerome shook his head self-disgustedly. 'I totally forgot to introduce Sapphie.' He turned to smile apologetically at the woman standing slightly behind him.

Rik hadn't even noticed the petite, auburn-haired figure until then—what man would when in the company of a golden goddess?

But as she stepped forward at Jerome's encouragement, shoulder-length auburn hair gleaming brightly in the sunlight, amber-coloured eyes gleaming like a cat's as she looked up at Rik challengingly, he felt the last vestiges of colour fade from his already pale face.

Today was already turning out as something of a shock; first the unexpected meeting with Dee and her husband, then the realisation that his love for Dee had died long ago. But now, with this other lady's appearance, it had just taken on nightmarish proportions!

Because he knew her.

He hadn't seen her for five years either, and their acquaintance had been brief—very brief!—but nevertheless he knew her.

In *every* sense of the word!

CHAPTER ONE

RIK PRINCE *had* recognised her, Sapphie realised with inner dismay as he continued to stare at her in disbelief.

Not that any of her own emotions showed—she kept her own expression deliberately bland, and betrayed none of her shock, or the effects of the painful memories that were flooding back: the love that had shaken her world apart after she had spent a night with this man. Most definitely, she showed none of the horror she felt inwardly at finding herself face to face with a man she had thought she'd never see again!

But then, it might have been OK if he hadn't so obviously recognised her *and* remembered too…!

Her small, pointed chin rose defensively as she thrust her hand out in greeting. 'Sapphie Benedict, Mr Prince,' she introduced herself with a pointedness that only a complete idiot could miss. And, despite the fact she knew that Rik Prince loved Dee to distraction, she didn't believe he *was* a complete idiot..just a selectively blind one!

Rik continued to stare at her, making no effort to take her outstretched hand, giving every impression of a man who had just been poleaxed.

Sapphie's direct stare turned to a glare as she mentally willed him to pull himself together and say something. Anything. Just staring at her in this way was sure to be noticed, and commented on, by the other couple who were with them, and—

'Miss Benedict,' Rik Prince finally bit out tautly after briefly touching her hand. 'Or is that Mrs...?'

'It's Miss,' she corrected abruptly, her hand dropping back to her side, unobtrusively massaging the slight tingling of her fingers where he had briefly touched her.

Incredible...! She couldn't believe, after all this time, that she could still be so totally aware of this man. It had been five years, for goodness' sake; she should have got over this long ago!

'Much too formal,' Jerome put in with cheerful reproach. 'Rik and Sapphie sounds much more friendly!'

Friendly was the last thing Sapphie wanted to be with Rik Prince! *Especially* with Rik Prince. Something she intended making clear to him at the earliest opportunity. In fact...

'Why don't you take Dee to see those accessories she was interested in, Jerome?' she encouraged lightly. 'Rik and I will order more coffee for us all, and by the time the two of you get back we may have managed to get on to a first-name basis!'

'You will join us for coffee, Rik...?' Dee prompted huskily.

Sapphie's brows rose as Rik dragged his gaze away from hers in order to answer Dee in the affirmative.

Really, did the man have no sense whatsoever? she wondered impatiently; Dee and Jerome's suspicions were sure to be aroused if he didn't stop behaving in this way.

Not that Jerome seemed to have noticed anything unusual as he turned, smiling, to his wife. 'Come on, honey, I want to buy you an anniversary present,' he encouraged Dee indulgently. Then the two of them departed to go shopping.

Leaving behind them the kind of silence that could be cut with a knife!

But what else could Sapphie have done but encourage Jerome to take Dee away from here—even though the last thing she wanted was to be left alone with Rik Prince? He certainly hadn't been playing his part in the drama of two strangers being introduced for the first time.

'I thought Dee and Jerome's wedding anniversary was in September.' Rik suddenly spoke as he turned back from watching the couple leave.

'It is,' Sapphie sighed, moving to sit down at the table where Dee's coffee was cooling. 'Please—join me,' she invited curtly as Rik Prince continued to stand in the middle of the pavement, as if unsure what to do next.

She had seen that dazed look before on dozens of men's faces after spending time looking at Dee—seen it and, in this case, lamented it.

She slipped her sunglasses up in her hair as she continued to look at Rik Prince. He was just as handsome as she remembered: perhaps slightly leaner, but his dark hair was still as vibrantly overlong, brushed carelessly back from his brow, and his eyes as deep blue, his good-looking face all strong angles, and his muscular frame visible beneath the faded denims and cream polo-shirt he wore.

Finally he moved, his movements fluid as he sat down in the chair facing hers, his expression under control now, his eyes guarded by lowered lids.

Sapphie gave a frustrated sigh at his continued silence. Jerome might have been unaware of the intimacy between Dee and this man a few minutes ago, but she certainly hadn't been. She also questioned whether the meeting had happened by chance; if anyone had known how devastated Rik Prince had been five years ago when Dee married Jerome, then it was her. He had been in love with Dee then, and Sapphie had every reason to believe he was still in love with her now.

'Today is the anniversary of the day Dee and Jerome first met,' Sapphie informed him softly.

'I see,' he bit out tautly, the expression in those deep blue eyes still unreadable.

Sapphie wasn't sure at that moment which of the sudden impulses she felt was the stronger—the need to shake or hit him!

It had been five years, for goodness' sake; surely he had got over his feelings for Dee by now?

It had to be obvious to anyone looking at Dee and Jerome that, for the most part, theirs was a happy marriage. It had its occasional hiccup—like any other marriage—but even in these days of quick divorces and remarriages, it had to be clear that Dee and Jerome were destined to last for some time yet.

'I never—'

'Before—'

They both began talking at once, only to come to an awkward stop, then stare enquiringly at the other.

'Please,' Sapphie invited before turning smilingly to the waiter to order more coffee, only to turn back and find Rik Prince looking at her in brooding silence. 'You were about to say something,' she reminded him, unnerved by his steadily intense stare.

He seemed to mentally shake himself, sitting up straighter in the cane chair. 'I was going to say that, after all this time, I never expected to see you again.'

Amusement curved her lips. 'You mean, you hoped never to see me again!'

He frowned. 'If I had meant to say that, then that's what I would have said.'

'Oh, please.' Sapphie brushed his protest away with a wave of her hand. 'The sentiment, I can assure you,' she told him with feeling, 'is mutual!' She had never wanted to see him again, never wanted to even hear of him again, just wanted to block his existence even from her memory.

And yet now that she had seen him and spoken to him, she could see just how dearly familiar were his dark good looks and piercing blue eyes. Too familiar…!

Rik gave a humourless smile. 'That's honest, at least,' he drawled drily.

'It's a trait too few people possess nowadays. And, continuing to be honest,' she added, 'what I was going to say just now was that I feel, before Dee and Jerome return, which won't be too long now, I should make it perfectly clear to you that under no circumstances—and I do mean that,' she emphasised firmly, 'do I wish for either of them to discover we ever knew each other before today.' She looked at him challengingly.

He frowned for several long seconds, and then his brow cleared as he looked at her with mocking blue eyes. 'By saying that the two of us knew each other, I take it you mean—'

'I mean,' she put in forcefully, 'that I would rather Dee and Jerome believed we met for the first time today,' she explained clearly and succinctly.

Rik Prince gave an acknowledging inclination of his head, whatever disadvantage he had felt earlier seeming to have evaporated as he relaxed back in his chair, his eyes clearly showing his amusement now.

Well, she was glad he could find something funny about this situation—because she certainly couldn't!

'How does that sit with the honesty you mentioned only seconds ago?' he ventured sardonically.

'Oh, don't be so obtuse!' Sapphie replied impatiently. 'There's a time for honesty, and—'

'A time for dishonesty?' Rik finished derisively.

'Please don't tell me you're any more anxious than I am to admit to Dee and Jerome that the two of us stupidly spent the night together after their wedding!' She was breathing deeply in her agitation as she glared at him.

But her impatient anger couldn't keep the memories at bay of that night, of no words having been spoken between them as they'd seemed drawn to each other like magnets, of the passion they'd shared—a fierce and wondrous passion, as they'd sought oblivion in each other's arms.

Even now Sapphie could remember each caress, each kiss, their need wild and uninhibited, both of them seeming to recognise and accept that, in the clear light of the following day, they would each go their separate ways, never to see one another again.

And that was how it should have remained. How, if she had had her way, it *would* have remained!

'That day, you had just seen the woman you love marry someone else!' she prompted angrily.

Colour darkened his cheeks, his eyes the blue-grey of a stormy sea now. 'And if I had?' he bit out icily. 'What was your excuse?'

She could be selective, make excuses, could even evade the issue. But the truth, she knew—or at least the part she was willing to admit to Rik!—was much more likely to put an end to this conversation. 'Me?' she echoed self-disgustedly. 'I had just watched the man I loved marry someone else!' She now met Rik's gaze unflinchingly.

Because it was only part of the truth of what had happened to her that day. Sapphie had gone to Dee and Jerome's wedding believing she was still in love with Jerome, and had felt nothing but misery as she'd watched him marrying Dee.

But then something—she wasn't sure what—had made her glance around the church, and her eyes had come to rest abruptly on Rik Prince as he'd stared broodingly down the aisle at the couple being married, obviously as unhappy about it as she was.

Until that moment, love at first sight had just been a phrase to Sapphie, not something that ever happened to real people like her. Well, except perhaps those people who realised the following morning, as they looked at the person beside them in bed, that it had probably been lust at first sight, rather than love!

She wasn't one of those people; she'd woken at dawn the morning after Dee and Jerome's wedding to gaze hungrily at the man sleeping beside her, knowing that not only did she love every hard plane and hollow that made up his physical being, but that she also loved his gentleness, his intelligence, and sense of honour too.

She had gone to the wedding the day before believing herself in love with one man, but after the celebration had realised that she was irrevocably in love with another.

A man who'd made no secret of the fact that he was in love with Dee...

Jerome?

Was Sapphie Benedict referring to Jerome Powers?

Sapphie, with her mesmerising, amber-coloured eyes, and her grim determination to discuss and dismiss their first and—until now—only other meeting, had been hurting as much as Rik had five years ago because she'd been in love with Jerome Powers? She'd spent the wedding reception with him, and the night with him, because she had just watched the man she loved marry someone else?

But hadn't he just admitted to having done the same thing? Wasn't that night—and Sapphie herself—something he had kept buried deep at the back of his consciousness, the door to it tightly locked and bolted?

Yes, of course it was. But that was because he had always felt guilty about that night, about the fact that he had used Sapphie as a way of blocking out his pain. Knowing she had used him in the same way added a dimension now that filled him with anger. His fury wasn't logical, and it certainly wasn't fair, but it was how he felt, none the less.

'Are you still in love with Powers?' Rik rasped contemptuously. 'Is that the reason you're still hanging around the two of them? Hoping to step into Dee's shoes if the marriage should falter?'

'How dare you?' Sapphie gasped incredulously, having paled dramatically, those amber eyes the only colour in her face now. 'For your information, Mr Prince, I'm not hanging around the two of them at all. I happen to have been in Paris for four days now, doing some research. Dee and Jerome decided to stop off here yesterday in order to see me on their way to Dee's film première in London next week.'

'How convenient for you,' Rik scorned.

He hadn't even attempted to see Dee since her wedding day five years ago, whereas this woman appeared to have remained friends with both Dee and Jerome. Masochistic or what?

'It isn't convenient at all,' Sapphie came back forcefully. 'And as for my wanting to step into Dee's shoes if the marriage should falter—if you listened to what I said just now, then you'll have realised I used the past tense concerning my feelings towards Jerome. I *was* in love with him then, but I'm not now.' She was breathing hard in her agitation, her eyes sparkling with anger.

Considering how defensive she was, Rik wasn't sure that he believed her.

But somehow, looking into those amber-coloured eyes and seeing the contempt gleaming there, he doubted Sapphie Benedict cared whether he believed her or not!

What was hard to believe, as he looked at her now, seeing how her eyes gleamed challengingly, twin spots of fiery colour burned her cheeks, and the fullness of her mouth had thinned to a taut line, was that he had ever explored every inch of that slenderly tiny body, that he had run his hands time and again through the auburn thickness of her shoulder-length hair, kissed every inch of her gamin-featured beauty and tasted the intimate delight of her luscious lips and mouth.

Sapphie, as if becoming aware of Rik's lingering gaze, of the thoughts running through his head, seemed to gather herself up to attack. 'Let me make one thing clear, Mr Prince—'

'I thought it was to be Rik and Sapphie,' he reminded her tauntingly, smiling his thanks at the waiter as he placed the pot of fresh coffee and cups down on the table.

'Mr Prince,' Sapphie enunciated carefully once they were alone again, 'I don't know you. I don't want to know you. Is that clear enough for you?'

She really was beautiful, Rik acknowledged slightly dazedly; not that he had thought—even five years ago when he needed to block out the pain—that he would have been attracted to someone who wasn't beautiful. It just came as a surprise to him now to realise quite *how* beautiful Sapphie Benedict was.

More beautiful than Dee? Well…no. But Dee's beauty was made up of golden hues, whereas this woman was all fire and light; her hair, for example, gleamed red as the sunlight caught it, and her eyes had taken on the colour of leaping flames.

There was also the fact that, notwithstanding how much in love he'd been with Dee five years ago, the two of them had never gone any further than a few clandestine kisses. Whereas he and Sapphie Benedict had shared the most complete intimacy there was between a man and a woman.

'Very clear, Sapphie,' he finally answered her slowly. 'But if that really was the case, how would I know about the birthmark you have on your—?'

'Will you stop that?' she snapped furiously, sitting forward. 'Dee and Jerome are on their way back now,' she hissed warningly after a brief glance over his shoulder. 'This conversation is over as far as I'm concerned!'

Rik turned to give a cursory glance in the direction of the married couple as they strolled along hand in hand, pausing to look in a store window now, his mouth twisting with distaste even as he acknowledged how right they looked together: Dee so tall and goldenly beautiful, Jerome with that natural confidence of a successful middle-aged man.

'I would keep that emotion under wraps too, if I were you,' Sapphie bit out impatiently. 'Jealousy can be so unattractive!'

Rik turned back to find her looking at him scathingly. Jealousy? Of Jerome's role as Dee's husband, was what Sapphie meant. Was he still jealous of Jerome? No, in all honesty, he couldn't say that he was, any more.

Did that mean that he really was over his love for Dee...?

He raised dark brows as he returned Sapphie Benedict's challenging look. 'You would know, I suppose,' he drawled mockingly, but took no pleasure in the way her face fell at his deliberate taunt.

How ironic, how absolutely incredible, that the two of them should both have been in love with other people five years ago. Although Sapphie denied that she still felt that way about Jerome. And he... He realised with another lightening of his heart that, without even knowing it, he'd got over Dee. She was still one of the most beautiful women he had ever seen, but he could now view that beauty dispassionately.

Sapphie eyed him dismissively now. 'I never took you for an idiot, Rik. Misguided in your love for Dee, perhaps, but never an idiot.'

He looked at her curiously. 'You don't like Dee very much, do you?' he realised wonderingly; he had never met anyone before, male or female, who didn't instantly fall under Dee's charming spell. Although being in love with the other woman's husband would probably do it, he allowed.

'Of course I like Dee,' Sapphie bristled resentfully. 'Knowing a person's weaknesses and faults doesn't preclude your liking them.'

Rik gave her a rueful grin. 'Knowing mine doesn't seem to have endeared me to you!'

She eyed him bleakly. 'There are always exceptions to every rule,' she retorted before turning to smile warmly at Dee and Jerome as they rejoined them, her expression affectionately indulgent as she took in the new handbag that Dee carried. 'I see you preferred the larger design,' Sapphie teased.

Dee grinned unabashedly, her pleasure in the gift obvious. 'If you're going to have a designer bag, then it may as well be a big one!' She dropped gracefully into the chair next to Sapphie before placing the new purchase on the table. 'Isn't it absolutely gorgeous?'

The white bag, printed with a pattern of the designer's motif in different colours, was certainly big, Rik acknowledged. However, it also wasn't the little purse initially suggested. But then, why shouldn't Dee choose a much more expensive number? Jerome was so rich he made the multimillionaire Prince brothers look like paupers!

'It's lovely,' Sapphie assured the other woman warmly.

Rik couldn't help but admire, on the other couple's return, the way in which Sapphie seemed to have shaken off her obvious animosity towards him. Anyone glancing in their direction now would be sure to think they were just four friends enjoying a cup of coffee together on this glorious Parisian day.

Rik wasn't actually quite sure whether he could really class the four of them as friends, given all the emotions teeming beneath their surface politeness!

Nevertheless, he was reluctant for their time together to end. It had taken five years for him to meet Sapphie Benedict again and—surprisingly!—he found he was so intrigued, that he didn't want there to be another five before it happened again!

'I was just suggesting to Sapphie,' he gave her a sideways glance, his mouth quirking humorously as he noticed the disapproving tightening of her full lips, 'that it would a good idea if the four of us were to have dinner together this evening.'

He had turned back to the married couple by the time he made this suggestion, so he didn't actually see Sapphie's reaction to his suggestion—but he certainly felt it!

Shock was quickly followed by waves of pure animosity in his direction which she made no effort to conceal!

CHAPTER TWO

'YOU'RE incredibly stupid or totally insane—and as I don't believe for a moment that it's the latter, I can only assume that it's the former!' Sapphie spoke vehemently even as she marched her way past Rik and into the sitting-room of his hotel suite, not sparing her obviously luxurious surroundings a second glance as she turned to glare at him.

'Come in, why don't you?' Rik drawled sardonically, taking his time about closing the door and joining her.

Giving Sapphie the opportunity to take in exactly how handsome he looked in the black evening suit and snowy white shirt and black bow-tie. Not that she hadn't ever noticed how devastatingly attractive he was, it was just that he just looked breathtakingly so in this formal attire, every inch the wealthy and powerful screenwriter that he was.

She had responded to the way he looked five years ago, but also to the way he'd made her feel; she'd been attracted to his inborn confidence and sophistication as much as to his handsome features. But this was something else entirely.

Now he wasn't just Rik Prince, the youngest, and reputedly the most sensitive, of the powerful Prince brothers; now he was also the link between herself and the past, between her and…

No, she mustn't even go there! She had spent a night of mindless passion with this man, and he had to believe that was all they had shared.

He arched dark brows now as he eyed her teasingly. 'Am I to take it from your previous remark that you aren't looking forward to the four of us having dinner together this evening?'

Looking forward to it—it had to be the worst torture she could ever imagine!

Spending hours in Rik's company. Aware all that time that he was probably still in love with Dee. In a constant state of agitation herself, in case either Dee or Jerome said anything that might arouse Rik's suspicions. No, she wasn't looking forward to it at all!

But when Rik had made his suggestion earlier about dinner at Fouquet's, and it was greeted with such enthusiasm by Dee and Jerome, Sapphie simply hadn't been able to think of a good reason for not joining them. Especially as it had already been agreed earlier in the morning that she would eat with Dee and Jerome tonight. Besides, she dared not dine with all of them, because she was still nervous that either Dee or Jerome might unwittingly say something about Matthew…

Even so, she was sure that Rik had known earlier exactly how she felt about having dinner with him, since she'd spent the rest of their meeting this morning in silence, nodding her agreement to the suggestion they all meet in the hotel foyer downstairs at eight o'clock.

'Idiot!' she snapped now, totally immune to his admiring glance as he took in the black sheath knee-length dress she was wearing, and the way her auburn hair fell loose on the bareness of her shoulders. She gave an impatient shake of her head. 'This is a dangerous game you're playing—'

'Dangerous?' Rik echoed, dark brows arched mockingly. 'You aren't suddenly going to launch yourself at me in a passionate frenzy, are you?'

'Oh, very funny,' Sapphie bit out disgustedly. 'You are such a funny man, Rik. In fact, with your wit, I'm surprised you've never turned your talent to writing comedies!'

He grinned unconcernedly, an endearing dimple appearing in one cheek, obviously feeling completely relaxed about the evening ahead. 'I've never really thought about it,' he shrugged, 'but now that you mention it...' He smiled in the face of her obvious frustration. 'It's a little early yet for us to go and meet Dee and Jerome; would you care for a drink before we leave?'

As it had turned out, Rik and Dee and Jerome were all staying at the George V, just off the Champs-Elysées, whereas Sapphie had decided to stay in a more obscure—and less expensive!—hotel in one of the avenues off the Arc de Triomphe, so it had been decided that the three of them would meet in the foyer of the George V before strolling along to the restaurant.

And yes, Sapphie was well aware of the fact that it was too early to meet the other couple. Deliberately so. As this man had to be well aware.

'A brandy would be nice,' she accepted abruptly, having already noticed the untouched bottles of whisky and brandy on one of the side-tables. 'Thank you,' she added awkwardly.

'So far this evening you've called me "incredibly stupid" and an "idiot"—don't you think it's a little late for politeness?' He eyed her laughingly.

Sapphie felt a leap of awareness in her chest at how very attractive he was in this teasingly friendly mood. It would be so easy to forget everything else, and just enjoy being in his company...

His company was something she dared not risk enjoying! In fact, she couldn't let her guard down for even a second, had been a mass of churning emotions since the moment they'd met again this morning, feeling as if she were remaining only two steps ahead of a tsunami—and while it was increasing in force she was tiring fast!

She had to find a way of stopping it—stopping Rik—in his tracks!

'Thank you,' she murmured again as she took the glass of brandy from his hand and took a sip of the fiery liquid, hoping it would give her the courage she so badly needed.

Courage...? She was going to need more than courage if she was going to completely alienate Rik Prince. And that was exactly what she had to do—if she could stop him finding her amusing long enough to do it, that was!

Under other circumstances, meeting Rik again could have been the highlight of her trip to Paris. But as it was...

'Mr Prince—'

'You know, you really can't carry on being so formal with a man you've shared a bed with,' he cut in smoothly.

And a sofa. And the floor. Even the shower—if her memory served her correctly. And she knew that it did.

All of which would be better forgotten, let alone talked about! 'Rik,' she corrected tautly, sitting down in one of the armchairs and instantly wishing she hadn't, as Rik's gaze was drawn to the amount of silk-covered thigh revealed by her dress riding up her legs. 'The danger I was referring to has nothing to do with me—'

'Pity,' he responded, relaxing back in an armchair himself now as he looked across at her with narrowed eyes.

'—and everything to do with Dee and Jerome,' Sapphie continued determinedly.

She had given this a lot of thought when she returned to her hotel earlier—in the circumstances, how could she possibly think of anything else?—and had decided she couldn't make this personal, otherwise Rik's suspicions would be aroused anyway. So she had decided to make Dee and Jerome the issue instead.

It seemed to be working as Rik's mouth tightened, his expression grim. 'What about them?' There was a definite edge to his voice now. 'As you've already been at great pains to point out to me, they are obviously a happily married couple.'

'Yes, they are.' Sapphie nodded. 'But beneath his genial façade, Jerome is a very jealous man.'

Rik gave a slight inclination of his head. 'Dee is a lot younger than him, and a very beautiful woman.'

'She can also be a very silly one,' Sapphie told Rik with feeling. 'Not that it's her fault,' she added, remembering all too well Rik's earlier accusation that she didn't like Dee. Of course she liked Dee, but if this was going to work, then she had to exaggerate some of Dee's less admirable traits. 'Dee was very overindulged as a child. Her father adored her, always referred to her as his perfect diamond.' Sapphie shook her head. 'Is it any wonder that she grew up expecting every other man to adore her, too?'

'I don't know,' Rik said slowly. 'Is it?'

'Of course it's not,' Sapphie shot back. She wasn't getting through to him at all! 'I mentioned earlier that Dee and Jerome have had their share of hiccups…? Well, those hiccups usually occur after one of Dee's—flirtations. Jerome, understandably, resents any man who gets too close to his wife.'

'Understandably,' Rik echoed tightly. 'Although I still don't see what this has got to do with me.'

Sapphie eyed him exasperatedly; this wasn't going at all as she had planned. She had intended giving Rik a little friendly advice—such as 'stay away from Dee because of Jerome's jealousy'!—and he obviously wasn't getting it at all. She felt like boxing his ears now!

'You're in love with Dee—'

'Am I?'

She frowned frustratedly. 'Of course you are!'

'If you say so.' He shrugged.

'Look, I'm trying to help you,' she pressed on impatiently.

'So it would appear.'

She sighed at his lack of cooperation. 'The last man to get too close to Dee ended up losing his job on the *New York Times* newspaper and going back writing about cattle shows in his home state of Texas!' A fate that was a vast improvement on the one that had befallen Dee's admirer before that, an actor who was sacked from his role in a major film and was now working behind the counter of a fast-food chain!

Rik looked amused. 'And you think that might happen to me?' he queried. 'It's very nice of you to be so concerned on my behalf, Sapphie, but it really isn't necessary.'

She really wasn't getting through to him, was she? So much for advising him to stay away from both Dee and Jerome—and, as a consequence, away from her too; he just seemed to find her advice amusing!

'I am not concerned about you,' she stood up, deciding to try a different tack; if he didn't care about himself, then perhaps he would care on Dee's behalf. 'It's Dee I'm worried about.' She glared down at him.

Rik returned her gaze with cool blue eyes, his thoughts now unreadable behind a cold mask.

'Are you telling me,' he finally spoke carefully, 'that Jerome is likely to become violent towards Dee if—?'

'No, of course I'm not,' Sapphie denied exasperatedly; she just seemed to be making this situation worse, not better. And she had thought it couldn't get any worse! 'For all that she's emotionally immature,

Dee really does love Jerome. Being older than her, he gives her the stability she felt she had lost when her father died—'

'You presume to know an awful lot about the emotions of the woman who married the man with whom you yourself were in love,' Rik rasped harshly.

Perhaps she was getting through to him after all.. he certainly didn't seem amused any more!

'I don't presume to know anything—'

'I think that you do.' Rik stood up in one fluid movement. 'And in the circumstances, I find your so-called concern for Dee a little—suspect, shall we say?'

He was very overbearing, towering over her like this, but Sapphie refused to back down now, finally feeling as if she was getting through to him. If she succeeded in getting him to back out of Dee's life— and consequently her own!—then she didn't care how intimidating he appeared!

'No, we will not say,' she replied tartly. 'As Dee's sister, of course I—'

'As her what?'

Sapphie instinctively took a step backwards at the vehemence in his tone, her eyes widening now as she took in the look of complete shock that he was too disturbed to even attempt to hide.

He hadn't known, she realised belatedly.

Incredibly, somehow, with everything else that had happened between them that night five years ago, she must have forgotten to mention that Dee was her little sister!

*   *   *

Sapphie was Dee's sister? The same stepsister who, along with her mother, had pressured Dee five years ago into going through with her marriage to Jerome Powers?

But wasn't that what she was doing now, too? Warning him, and every other man by the sound of it, from going anywhere near Dee's marriage to Jerome.

'Your name is Benedict, not McCall,' he finally bit out forcefully. Stupidly. Dee was an actress; McCall probably wasn't even her real name. But it seemed so impossible that these two women, so totally physically different, could possibly be related in any way, let alone be sisters!

'We're half-sisters,' Sapphie told him dismissively. 'I was two years old when my mother married Fergus McCall. Dee was born a year later.'

Rik turned away to walk over to the window, staring sightlessly out into the Parisian night.

Damn it, he had been congratulating himself earlier on the fact that he was over whatever he had felt for Dee, that, without him even being aware of it, his emotions had moved on.

And now this!

He hadn't asked Sapphie five years ago what she was doing at Dee and Jerome's wedding, whether her connection was to either the bride or groom. In fact, they hadn't talked much at all, he realised now.

But, thinking back to that time, remembering the things Dee had told him about her stepmother and stepsister, of how they were pressurising her into marrying the rich and powerful Jerome Powers, he couldn't help but wonder if his meeting with Sapphie that night had been quite as by chance as it had appeared at the time...

'Let me guess.' Sapphie spoke behind him. 'If Dee spoke of her family at all, it was to regale you with the stepmother and stepsister story?' She grimaced as he turned sharply back to face her. 'My stepfather died when Dee was thirteen.' She gave a sad shake of her head. 'His death hit her very hard, and the only way she could deal with it at the time was to think of herself as the beautiful swan left in the nest of the ugly ducklings! It seemed harmless enough at the time, if a little hurtful to our mother.'

The picture she was painting of Dee wasn't a pretty one. Rik remembered Dee as a beautiful butterfly desperately trying to fly away from the two women who were trying to run her life for her.

This woman and her mother!

But her mother and half-sister, not stepmother and stepsister...

He gave a dismissive shake of his head; if he once started to doubt Dee's integrity five years ago, then he really was in trouble!

Sapphie gave a humourless smile. 'I can see that you don't believe me.'

It wasn't a question of believing or not believing her; he was newly coming to terms with the fact that he was no longer in love with Dee, and also with hearing Sapphie telling him that the woman he had thought himself in love with all those years ago had never really existed either—it was just too much to take in!

'Why the hell should I?' he came back harshly. 'You and your mother got your way five years ago, let's just leave it at that, shall we?'

Sapphie looked perplexed now. 'My mother? What does she have to do with any of this?'

'Oh, please!' he grated.

And to think he had actually been starting to like Sapphie, to admire the cool way she'd dealt with what had happened between them five years ago. Hell, he was no longer even sure that it had just happened between them all those years ago; in fact, the more he thought about the way they had met, their lack of conversation, that shared passion in his hotel suite, the more he began to wonder if it hadn't all been planned to keep him well and truly occupied while Dee married someone else.

Although this presupposed that Dee's mother and sister had been aware that there was someone else in Dee's life besides Jerome...

Damn it, he had to get out of here—before he let those thoughts take him where he didn't want to go and he actually resorted to strangling Sapphie Benedict for what he now suspected her motives might have been towards him all those years ago!

'It's time to go,' he instructed after a glance at his wrist-watch. 'Dee and Jerome will be wondering where we are.'

Sapphie looked up at him uncertainly. 'Rik, what—?'

'I said it's time to go!' he commanded, grasping hold of her arm and manoeuvring her towards the door, allowing no respite when she stumbled slightly trying to pick up her evening bag.

He was too angry at this moment, needed to be where there were other people. Because strangling was probably too good for this woman.

But kissing her, at the same time showing his contempt for her, certainly wasn't!

He came to an abrupt halt as he reached the door, turning Sapphie Benedict in his arms to lower his head and take possession of her lips with his.

It was a kiss that wasn't meant to be enjoyed, by either of them. And as Rik felt Sapphie tremble in his arms he knew that she certainly wasn't deriving any pleasure from it, that if anything she was wary of him, of where his anger might take them. Well, let her be wary. She deserved to be wary. He wanted her to be wary. He wanted to take her…

His deeper, inner, decent self took control at that moment, filling him with self-disgust for the way he was behaving. He had never treated a woman like this in his life before, but as he felt the shuddering sobs that shook Sapphie's slender body he knew that he was both hurting and humiliating her. Not that she didn't deserve that—and worse—for what she and her mother had done five years ago; he just didn't intend lowering himself to her level.

He wrenched his mouth away from hers, taking hold of her upper arms to push her away from him, emotion blazing in his eyes as he saw the wretchedness of her expression, her eyes glittering with unshed tears, her lips puffy and obviously kissed.

An act. It was all an act, he assured himself determinedly; this woman, as much as Jerome Powers, had robbed him of Dee, of the love they had once shared—and he would never forgive her for it.

He drew in a harsh breath. 'If you're expecting an apology—'

'I'm not!' She wrenched out of his grasp, stepping away from him, the colour returning to her cheeks. 'I don't expect anything from you. I never have,' she added bleakly.

Rik's eyes narrowed. 'And what the hell is that supposed to mean?'

She made a dismissive movement with her hand. 'Nothing. Absolutely nothing.'

It wasn't nothing. It had certainly been something, a slight undertone to that comment that he couldn't quite put a name to…

But he could put a name to how he was feeling— and it wasn't pretty. He had never had cause to feel ashamed of his actions before, but he certainly wasn't proud of the way he had treated Sapphie just now. Even if she did deserve his contempt. She and her mother both.

Except…

Again he thought of the fact that Sapphie's mother was also Dee's mother, and that neither were the step-sister and stepmother Dee had claimed them to be. Why had she lied to him about those relationships? He—

'Dee and Jerome will be waiting for us downstairs,' Sapphie reminded him softly.

Rik frowned darkly at the way Sapphie avoided actually meeting his gaze, effectively making him feel more of a heel than ever.

Though he didn't see why he should, he decided as his resolve returned. Not when this woman, along with her mother, were responsible for it not being 'Dee and Rik' who were waiting downstairs.

'Then we had better go and join them, hadn't we?' he returned, his mouth twisting grimly as Sapphie stepped back to avoid the hand he would have placed beneath her elbow.

Fine. He didn't want to touch her again, anyway. Still couldn't be responsible for his actions where Sapphie Benedict was concerned!

CHAPTER THREE

'YOU'RE very quiet this evening, Sapphie; is there anything wrong?'

Sapphie turned to look at her brother-in-law, forcing a smile to her lips as he looked at her concernedly.

Quiet? Jerome thought she was quiet? Well, maybe, but Dee and Rik had talked enough for all of them during the last couple of hours as they dined together, usually about people or things of which Sapphie had no knowledge. Rik was completely ignoring the advice she had tried to give him earlier.

Oh, well, it had only been a case of misdirection on her part, an effort to try and draw attention away from herself. And she had been insulted and treated with suspicion for her pains. Why, she still didn't understand...

'I have a slight headache,' she excused, giving Jerome a reassuring smile. 'In fact—'

'You have a headache?' Dee prompted as she took time out from her laughing conversation with Rik. 'I have some tablets in my bag you can take.' She began to root through it. The new designer handbag, of course.

'I don't think that would be a good idea when I've already had a couple of glasses of wine,' Sapphie refused politely. 'In fact, I was just about to make my excuses and leave. A good night's sleep is probably all I need.' And to get away from Rik Prince's oppressive company!

She doubted if Dee and Jerome had noticed, but Rik hadn't so much as spoken one word to her during the last couple of hours. Not that she had wanted him to, but she was finding his silence towards her more unnerving than anything he might have said to her. That, and the brooding way Jerome had been watching his wife and Rik as they'd talked so easily together.

Dee, Sapphie knew, was always in her element when flirting with a man.

Rik Prince had been so wrong earlier when he'd accused her of not liking Dee. She loved her younger sister very much; she was just very aware of the emotional games Dee liked to play. And of Jerome's reaction to them.

She might have been using Jerome's jealousy earlier when she spoke to Rik as a diversion tactic, but actually Jerome's possessiveness where his wife was concerned was all too real.

It was a trait that had never shown its ugly face when Sapphie had believed herself to be in love with Jerome; if it had, she would have fallen out of love with him all the sooner. Although disillusionment had come soon enough: it was difficult to remain in love with someone who obviously loved someone else to distraction.

Although Rik Prince didn't seem to be having any trouble doing exactly that where Dee was concerned...!

'I'm really sorry to break up the party,' Sapphie

announced lightly, placing her napkin on the table-top and picking up her evening bag, 'but I really think it would be better if I went back to my hotel now.'

'I'll walk with you.'

Sapphie was so stunned by the fact that Rik had finally spoken to her, let alone by his offer to walk her back to her hotel, that her hand moved suddenly and knocked one of the wine glasses on the table. It would have fallen over, spilling its contents, had Rik not reached out and caught it as it began to tip.

Sapphie looked across at him with startled eyes. 'I'll be perfectly OK walking back alone.' After all, she had walked over to the George V by herself ear-lier!

'Oh, but I insist.' He easily held her gaze as he stood up, his expression unreadable. 'It's far too late for a woman to be out walking on her own. Besides,' he continued as Sapphie would have argued, 'I'm sure that Dee and Jerome have had quite enough company for one evening; this is romantic Paris, after all!'

Exactly, so why on earth would Rik want to stroll up the Champs-Elysées with her, of all people? Dee wasn't too happy at the prospect of losing her ad-mirer, either, if her pouting expression was anything to go by! And when Dee was upset about something, anyone standing in her way had better watch out!

Not that Sapphie was a willing participant in this current situation, but she knew from experience that wouldn't matter to Dee if she felt like hitting out...

'Don't be so silly, Rik,' Dee told him impatiently. 'Jerome and I have been to Paris dozens of times before!'

'And no doubt we'll come back dozens of times more, too,' Jerome put in emolliently. 'But Rik does have a point,' he smiled at his wife, 'a nice stroll beside the river, with the illuminated Eiffel Tower as a backdrop, would be very romantic.'

'Lucky you, Dee,' Sapphie told her quickly as she saw the rebellious sparkle in her sister's eyes; Dee clearly wasn't happy with the thought of Sapphie disappearing off into the night with her admirer. Well, Dee needn't worry; Sapphie intended dumping that admirer as soon as it was safe to do so.

Dee looked at her husband and his encouraging smile, then at Rik's bland expression, obviously trying to weigh up whether or not she wanted to create a scene by insisting that Rik stay. Sapphie held her breath as she waited for the result of that deliberation.

'That sounds wonderful, darling,' Dee finally breathed huskily, her fingers moving caressingly on her husband's arm now.

Causing Sapphie to breathe an inner sigh of relief. One thing maturity seemed to have done for Dee was to teach her when not to push her luck. Or perhaps not; Sapphie winced as Dee gave Rik a challenging smile—maybe her sister was just trying to make Rik jealous now?

One day, Sapphie was sure, this was all going to blow up in Dee's beautiful face. But not tonight, she noted with relief. Jerome seemed quite happy now that he was going to have his wife to himself for a while. Rik Prince's expression was much harder to read...

Well, if he was less than satisfied with his companion, that was his problem, not hers!

'You can leave now,' Sapphie told him tersely once they had walked a short distance down the wide avenue towards the Arc de Triomphe. 'Dee and Jerome have already disappeared in the opposite direction,' she added as Rik looked at her with raised brows.

There had been quite a lot of kissing, and 'we'll meet again tomorrow' as Dee and Jerome took their leave outside the restaurant. But Sapphie saw no reason to continue this charade now that the other couple were no longer around.

Besides, she really did have a headache, mainly due, she knew, to Rik Prince's tense silence as he walked beside her, hands thrust into his trouser pockets.

Probably a ploy to stop himself from reaching out and throttling her, Sapphie accepted ruefully; he had certainly looked as if that was what he would have liked to do to her in his hotel suite earlier this evening!

But instead of that, he had kissed her…

A kiss that was not meant to be enjoyed—by either of them.

And Sapphie really hadn't enjoyed it. But she had learnt something about herself that she would much rather not have known. Until tonight, until Rik kissed her again, she had believed that instant love she felt for him five years ago had withered and died through lack of nurturing. But tonight, held once more in Rik Prince's arms, she knew that wasn't the case at all.

She was as much in love with Rik now as she had been that night long ago!

Rik had absolutely no idea what he was doing walking along beside Sapphie!

It had been one of the strangest evenings he had ever known in his life.

On the one hand, there he'd been with Dee, the woman he'd believed himself in love with for the last five years—though now he knew that he no longer loved her at all.

Then there'd been Jerome, the man Dee had married instead of him: a man that Rik couldn't help but like.

And lastly there'd been Sapphie Benedict, a woman he had spent a burning night of passion with five years previously; Dee's half-sister. One of the women who had played a leading part in taking Dee from him all those years ago. He was still so angry about that, he hadn't even been able to bring himself to talk to her this evening!

Instead he had spoken to Dee, whom he could now view with dispassion—and with whom, he realised, he had absolutely nothing in common! Her conversation was of fashion and the artificial world of acting, from which he normally chose to distance himself.

Adding to his confusion was his disgust with himself for the way he had treated Sapphie earlier, which had been building up inside him all evening.

Yes, at the time he had been angry with Sapphie, suspicious of her motives for what had happened be-

tween them five years ago. And yes, the pain of that
had erupted out of control. But the way he had behaved, the physical retribution he had exacted,
seemed more in keeping with his eldest brother Nik's
ruthless nature than his own. Rik was the serious, caring, sensitive one of the family, not some arrogant
monster who heaped vengeance on anyone who got
in the way of what he wanted.

At least, that was what he had believed of himself
until earlier tonight…

He gritted his teeth and turned to Sapphie. 'I owe
you an apology—'

'I believe we've already had this conversation,
Rik,' Sapphie dismissed. 'I think we agreed that you
don't owe me anything!' she added bleakly.

There it was again, he recognised frowningly, that
something in her voice that he couldn't quite put a
name to…

'I do owe you an apology,' he insisted firmly, his
hands clenched into fists inside his trouser pockets. 'I
don't— I have never in my life before behaved towards any woman in the way that I did to you earlier
tonight.'

Sapphie shrugged her slender shoulders. 'I'm sure
that at the time you believed you had due provoca-
tion.'

'Whether I did or not is totally…' Rik broke off
frustratedly, breathing hard, realising that even his
apology was coming out all wrong.

What was it about this woman that made him behave so uncharacteristically? He really had no idea—
and he wasn't sure that he wanted to know, either!

He sighed his impatience. 'Sapphie, will you, for goodness' sake, just let me apologise?'

She gave him a cool glance. 'If it makes you feel better.'

'It isn't a question of making me feel better…!' But wasn't it? Wasn't he just trying to salvage his own conscience, rather than anything else? After all, his anger was no less now than it had been earlier; he had just been unnerved by his reaction. He hadn't even known he was capable of behaving in that coldly ruthless way. 'What sort of name is Sapphie, anyway?' he challenged in order to give himself time to think.

Amber eyes sparkled with amusement as she glanced up at him. 'Can't you guess?' she said drily.

'No, I— Sapphie…' he said slowly, wincing as the penny finally dropped. 'Short for Sapphire?'

'Short for Sapphire,' she acknowledged with a rueful smile.

'Diamond and Sapphire,' Rik murmured slightly incredulously; he had thought his own family names slightly bizarre, but naming your daughters after precious stones seemed even more so.

'It could have been worse,' she said. 'We could have been Ruby and Emerald!'

'Hm,' he grimaced. 'No doubt when you have children of your own you will name them Mary and John!'

'No doubt,' she replied stiffly, coming to an abrupt halt on the wide pavement to turn and look at him. 'There really is absolutely no need for you to walk me back to my hotel,' she told him determinedly.

'I've been on my own in Paris for four days without needing an escort!'

Her relaxed amusement, while they had been discussing her name, was gone now, her eyes as hard and glittering as the amber stone they resembled, her expression aloof.

Rik gave a slightly dazed shake of his head, having no idea what he had said or done this time to cause her withdrawal. But he had obviously done something; she had seemed almost friendly there for a few minutes.

Or maybe it was just remembered past intimacies that made any prolonged exchange between them difficult?

Despite his feelings for Dee, Rik hadn't led a celibate life the last five years. And each time he'd become involved with someone, he had hoped that she would be the one to overshadow the love he felt for Dee. It had never happened, of course—although meeting Dee again seemed to have done the trick; perhaps he should have arranged this meeting a long time ago! But he could never remember this present awkwardness happening with any of the other women he had been involved with, either at the end of their affair or afterwards. In fact, he had become quite good friends with some of them.

Somehow he couldn't ever see becoming friends as a possibility where Sapphie Benedict was concerned!

He straightened. 'Look, I'm sure that both you and your mother believed you were acting in Dee's best interests five years ago—'

'And I'm sure,' Sapphie cut in impatiently, 'that

despite the fact you've mentioned this several times today already, I have absolutely no idea what you're talking about!'

Rik scowled at her obstinacy. This really was asking too much. He was trying his best to salvage something out of this mess, to smooth things over between them, if only so that they could be polite to each other in front of other people. But Sapphie certainly wasn't doing anything to help the situation!

'You and your mother wanted Dee to marry Jerome—'

'I did?' Sapphie's eyes widened incredulously at this accusation. 'And why, when I was in love with him myself, would I have wanted her to do that?'

Rik frowned. It was a good point. In fact, it was a very good point. And, as he hadn't known of Sapphie's feelings towards Jerome until earlier today, it wasn't one he had thought about before, either.

But now he did and had, and the answers that came immediately to mind once again put a question mark over Dee's integrity five years ago. In the circumstances, that wasn't acceptable to him. It couldn't be. Because it made a lie of the love he had felt for her.

'I don't suppose it really mattered, as long as one daughter was married to him—and, of course, his vast wealth and media influence!'

'How dare you?' Sapphie gasped angrily, breathing hard, the curve of her breasts visible above the low neckline of her strapless dress.

A fact Rik was all too aware of as he looked down at her. She really was a firebrand, he acknowledged admiringly. In more ways than one, if his memory served him correctly. And he knew that it did.

Just as he was sure Sapphie remembered the night they had spent together. No matter how he wished it were otherwise, he knew there was no way they could ever meet as just casual acquaintances!

He gave a regretful sigh. 'Listen to me, Sapphie—'

'No, Rik, I want you to listen to me,' she cut in forcefully, every curvaceous inch of her rigid with anger. 'I have little idea what Dee told you about our family five years ago—although from the few things you've told me, I can certainly take a guess!' she said disgustedly.

'Believe it or not, at the time we had more important things to discuss than you and your mother!' he told her stiffly, already disturbed by the variations he had already discovered today in Dee's version of things.

'I'm sure,' she scorned. 'But now I'm telling you how it really was. At the time I lived and worked in America. I was Jerome's assistant. I was also his fiancée—'

'His fiancée?' Rik was too surprised to successfully cover his surprise.

She nodded. 'We flew back to England so that I could introduce him to my family. But once Jerome took one look at Dee, I knew that was the end of that.' She grimaced. 'Trying to stop the two of them falling in love would have been like standing in the way of an express train! Instead I decided to just bow out gracefully.' She looked up directly into Rik's eyes. 'You seem to have the idea it happened differently. It seems I can't do or say anything to change your opinion. What I can do, though,' she continued as he would have spoken, 'is assure you that my conscience—and, incidentally, that of my mother—is completely clear. Can you claim the same?'

Rik was still trying to take in all that she had just said. Sapphie had been engaged to marry Jerome and then had lost him to Dee? It was so different from Dee's version of events. But, at the same time, this made so much more sense than Dee's story about being forced into marriage with someone she didn't love—especially since Rik had been there for her, and professing his own love. Really, he couldn't help but doubt Dee's tale of what had happened.

Which brought into question the last five wasted years he had spent believing himself to be in love with Dee; had the woman he'd thought she was ever really existed?

The pugnaciousness of Sapphie's tone brought him back to reality. 'What do you mean?'

Her mouth quirked. 'Is this meeting-up in Paris with Dee quite the accident that it appears…?'

It didn't take too much effort to know what she was getting at. 'I do not have affairs with married women!'

'Not even if you're in love with them?' Sapphie taunted.

'Not even then!' But he wasn't still in love with Dee. He didn't know how he felt towards her any more. If what Sapphie said was true, then the love he'd thought he felt for Dee had been based on lies…Dee's lies…

'You don't believe me, do you?' Sapphie said.

'I didn't say that,' Rik grated.

He didn't want to believe it, that it was true, and yet…

Sapphie kept going. 'I wonder if Dee even knew how much you loved her…'

Or really cared!

The thought popped into his head completely unbidden, and now that it was there he couldn't seem to blank it out again. He had been in misery that day nearly five years ago when Dee had married Jerome. But, as far as he could see, Dee had been every inch the blushing bride, not so much as giving him a sideways glance. At the time he had thought it was because she didn't want to give the two of them away, but now he wondered if she had even been aware he was there, let alone the pain he was in.

All these years he had taken Dee's silence to mean that she was doing the best she could to get on with her life, just as she expected him to get on with his. But had that really been the case, or had Dee simply forgotten he existed?

What a fool he had been, if that was true!

His mouth tightened at what he saw as his own stupidity. 'I would rather leave my feelings for Dee out of this.' Especially as he no longer even knew what those feelings were!

'Can we do that? Could we ever do that?' Sapphie responded tightly. 'Besides, I don't even know what "this" is. Look, I realise it was a shock for you today to see me again after all this time, and to realise that I'm actually Dee's sister. But if you look at it logically, then you'll see that there's really no reason why the two of us should ever meet again. In fact,' she continued, 'it's amazing that it ever happened at all!' She didn't look any more pleased about it than he did.

Amazing wasn't quite the way Rik would have put it!

'Oh, do cheer up, Rik,' Sapphie admonished brightly, her eyes gleaming now. 'By this time tomorrow we can forget we ever did meet again. You see, there's a bright side to everything, if you only look hard enough!'

At this moment, his head full of conflicting impressions of Dee and this woman standing in front of him—a woman with whom he'd shared a night of passion—Rik couldn't for the life of him see the bright side!

CHAPTER FOUR

'WHAT on earth are you doing here?' Sapphie showed
her displeasure at having been shown out to the ter-
race of the George V, where she was expecting to
have breakfast with Dee and Jerome but instead had
found Rik Prince sitting at the table set for four.

Alone.

Not the sort of shock she needed first thing in the
morning!

Especially after the sleepless night she had just
spent, going over and over in her mind her conversation with Rik the previous evening in an effort to
see if she had said too much, or revealed more than
she intended. That was what she had been afraid of
all along, of course.

She had finally come to the conclusion that she
hadn't said anything that would rouse his suspicions...

Rik put his coffee-cup down on the table, clearly
no more pleased to see her than she was him. 'It may
have escaped your notice, Sapphie,' he drawled
hardly, 'but, unlike you, I happen to be a guest at this
hotel!'

Sapphie had half expected—and prepared herself!—for seeing him again at some stage during her
breakfast with Dee and Jerome. But she just hadn't
been expecting him to be sitting here and expecting

to eat with them. And all before she had even had her first cup of coffee of the day too!

'Jerome called me earlier this morning and suggested I have breakfast with him and Dee. At the time I couldn't think of any reason not to,' Rik confessed, confirming Sapphie's suspicions as she reluctantly sat down on the chair the waiter pulled back for her. 'I don't believe there was any mention of your being here too.' Otherwise he wouldn't be here either, his tone implied. A tone Sapphie chose to ignore as she turned smilingly to the waiter and ordered another pot of coffee; she had a feeling she was going to need it!

'Rather a sudden decision of theirs to go on to London later today, isn't it?' Rik opined, once the two of them were alone.

Sapphie had been a little surprised herself when Jerome had called her on her mobile and explained the reason for them breakfasting together, because the couple had originally planned to spend another couple of days in Paris.

Although perhaps, given Rik Prince's unexpected presence here, it wasn't so surprising, after all…

Jerome was, on the surface, the most genial of men, and his indulgence towards his wife seemed boundless. But Sapphie had been perfectly serious when she'd warned Rik that Jerome drew the line at pandering to Dee's flirtations.

Having witnessed her sister unashamedly leading Rik on the previous evening, Sapphie knew that Jerome would have had to have been blind not to see it too. Admittedly, despite talking to Dee exclusively,

Rik hadn't seemed to be giving her sister any encouragement.

Sapphie eyed Rik assessingly now. 'Isn't it?' she came back noncommittally, smiling her gratitude at the waiter as he poured her coffee before putting the pot down and departing.

Rik's gaze narrowed. 'And what's that supposed to mean?'

'Rik, I'm really not going to get into an argument with you before I've even had my coffee!'

He continued to look at her for several seconds, and then he gave a begrudging smile. 'It really isn't surprising that I never guessed you and Dee are related; besides the fact that you look absolutely nothing like each other, you really are nothing alike. I certainly can't imagine having a conversation like this with her!'

Sapphie sipped her coffee before answering, not sure whether or not to take his remark as a criticism. But considering that Rik seemed to think Dee was just about perfect—apart from the little fact that she already had a husband, of course—it probably was!

'Feeling better now?' he prompted mockingly as she rapidly finished one cup of coffee and poured herself another.

'Not particularly, no,' she answered flatly; where were Dee and Jerome?

Nine o'clock, Jerome had told her when he rang her earlier, and it was already ten minutes past now.

Rik grinned at her disgruntled attitude. 'Perhaps we should just go ahead and order breakfast? I noticed you hardly ate any dinner last night, so you're probably hungry.'

Sapphie gave him a sharp look, not having been aware that he had noticed anything the previous evening except Dee.

And that, she realised with an inner feeling of panic, felt distinctly like jealousy on her part!

No such thing, she instantly assured herself. What was the point of her feeling jealous about this man? Her feelings for him were going nowhere. Nowhere that she could allow them to go, anyway!

She put her coffee-cup down again. 'Shouldn't we wait for Dee and Jerome?'

'Mr Prince?' The waiter had once again appeared silently beside their table. 'Mr Powers has just telephoned down, sir,' he continued as Rik looked up at him enquiringly. 'He sends his apologies, but he and Mrs Powers aren't going to be able to join you, after all. He hopes that you and Miss Benedict will continue without them.'

An awkward silence followed the man's departure as Sapphie suddenly had an idea of what Jerome was trying to do, and Rik, she was sure, was desperately searching for a way to extricate himself from this situation!

'Hm,' he mused slowly. 'What's all that about, do you think? Why didn't Jerome call one of us directly on our mobiles?'

Sapphie had to admire Rik's shrewdness; most men wouldn't have realised that it was about anything!

But she didn't need to think about it herself; suddenly she knew exactly what Jerome was up to. It would have been laughable, if only Jerome hadn't chosen Rik Prince, of all people, to try and match make her with!

Ever since their broken engagement five years ago, Jerome had been suffering from a guilt complex where Sapphie was concerned, feeling as if he had let her down when he married Dee instead of her.

The result was that, whenever he could, Jerome sent an eligible bachelor in her direction, in the hope that she would fall in love. Rik Prince, it seemed, was his latest effort, and probably an attempt to kill two birds with one stone; if only he could encourage Rik to be attracted to Sapphie, Jerome would succeed at diverting the other man's attentions away from Dee!

However, Jerome couldn't possibly know that Rik Prince was the very last man Sapphie would ever allow into her life!

Into her own life. And into Matthew's…

Because she had no idea what Rik would say, what he would do, if he was to know that exactly nine months after they had spent the night together she had given birth to a healthy eight-pound baby boy.

Matthew.

Rik's son.

Sapphie had asked herself many times during her pregnancy whether or not she ought to contact Rik Prince about his impending fatherhood. A part of her said he had a right to know, but another part of her had argued strongly against it. Rik had made no effort to seek her out since their night together, had obviously never given a thought to the fact there might be any long-term consequences. If he had, perhaps her decision would have been a different one.

As it was, she had decided against telling him. It wasn't a night she was particularly proud of. She might have fallen in love with Rik on sight, but anyone with eyes in their head on Dee and Jerome's wedding day could have seen that Rik had had eyes for no one but the bride.

Sapphie had set out to deliberately bring herself to Rik's attention at the reception party, had noted his increasingly reckless mood as the evening wore on, even his invitation for her to join him in his hotel suite had been made in an offhand manner, as if he hadn't really cared whether she did or not.

The consequences of that night, she had argued to herself two months later when she'd learnt of her pregnancy, were hers alone. In fact, she had adamantly refused to tell anyone who the father of her baby was.

And when Matthew had been born, so beautiful, his hair dark and soft, with eyes the colour of the sky, she had been glad that she had decided not to tell Rik he was to be a father. This baby would be hers, and only hers.

It would have been too much to subject her beautiful child to a tug of war; even then she had known Rik well enough to know that was what it would have become, that he wasn't the sort of man to shirk his responsibilities. Matthew was too wonderful to ever be classed as someone's responsibility!

Which was the reason it had been such a shock to

see Rik again yesterday, why she had been desperately trying to alienate him ever since.

Unsuccessfully.

But one glance at him and she had seen how like his father Matthew already was; tall for his four years, his baby features already starting to show signs of the strength of his father's jaw, his mouth a perfect replica of Rik's, as was the deep blue of his eyes.

In fact, she had realised with a sickening lurch of her stomach, if anyone were to see Rik and Matthew together, their relationship would be unmistakable!

Not that she thought for a moment that Jerome had guessed the truth, and that was the reason for his trying to push Rik and her together; Dee and Jerome had last seen Matthew almost eighteen months ago, and he'd been very much a baby then. Also she was sure that the other couple really didn't have any idea that Sapphie and Rik had ever met before.

Something she had been at great pains to emphasise to Rik when she spoke to him yesterday. In fact, she felt as if she had been balancing on a tightrope since meeting Rik again.

But the worst part had definitely been the dread that either Dee or Jerome might mention her son, and that Rik would add two and two together and come up with the correct answer of four!

It hadn't happened, thank goodness, and luckily for her—and for obvious reasons of his own—Rik was no more anxious to reveal their past association than she was.

With any luck, with Dee and Jerome's departure

from Paris later today, Sapphie need never think of, or see, Rik Prince again!

And the sooner she got back to the house she and Matthew shared with her mother, to the peace and happiness that was their normal existence, the better she would like it!

'What do you think it's all about?' She answered Rik's question, deliberately turning the focus back to him and away from herself; he wouldn't be any more pleased by Jerome's matchmaking than she was.

Rik eyes narrowed, his mouth thinning. 'No matter what you may think to the contrary, Sapphie, I do not want to be, nor have I ever been, involved with a married woman!'

No, she could believe that, Sapphie accepted; he was too sincere for it not to be the truth. Which meant that he and Dee probably hadn't met again since Dee's marriage…

Not that it made a great deal of difference to her decision concerning Matthew. Guilt on Rik's part was not something either of them needed. Or pity, either.

Sapphie had had to rethink her life and career once she'd discovered she was pregnant and had decided to keep her baby, had known that her high-powered new job a personal assistant—Dee had insisted that Sapphie couldn't possibly continue to work for Jerome in the circumstances!—was not a suitable one for a single mother.

Even if she did say so herself, her career change, to a freelance society reporter, had worked out very well. She had made so many contacts and friends during her time as Jerome's assistant that finding people to interview hadn't been a problem, and neither had finding newspapers and magazines to publish her work. Jerome's publications had been amongst them, her brother-in-law assuring her that what Dee didn't know couldn't hurt her. And, as Sapphie had no personal contact with Jerome, she hadn't felt that she was betraying her sister's trust in any way either.

From writing those articles and meeting all those glamorous people—in some cases, unbelievably glamorous—had come the idea for writing a book. Ambitious, she knew, but it had been amazing how popular a novel with murder in Hollywood as its main theme had proved to be…

She gave Rik a scathing glance. 'I don't think I'm the one you have to convince of that,' she scorned. 'Do you?'

Rik was growing more than a little tired of bearing the brunt of Sapphie's derision. Especially as *he* was the one with a grievance, since he was still not completely convinced of her innocence when it came to what had happened five years ago.

He had thought over what she had said last night—in fact, he hadn't been able to sleep for thinking about it. But if he was to accept what Sapphie claimed had happened five years ago, if he was to believe her version of things, then that made him nothing but the idiot she had once claimed him to be, for believing in Dee so absolutely. And he wasn't ready to admit to that. Not yet.

But one thing he was willing to admit, to himself at least, was that he had never yet been bored in

Sapphie's company. As he had been by Dee's last night…?

Well…yes. But, he had also decided during his wakeful hours last night, maybe it was the five years' gulf between himself and Dee that had made it impossible for them to converse easily. That, and the presence of Dee's husband and sister!

'I think you're exaggerating Jerome's concern about Dee,' he rasped harshly, leaning back in his chair to look at Sapphie through narrowed eyes.

If she had suffered from any sleeplessness last night because of their previous heated exchanges, then it certainly didn't show, Sapphie looking refreshingly lovely this morning in a cream sundress that deepened her tan and brought out the red highlights in her hair, those amber eyes still clear and shining.

Damn it, her eyes were always challenging when she looked at him. Something else he was finding he disliked intensely.

Sapphie's feelings for Jerome Powers all those years ago could hardly have been mild, considering she had been engaged to him. In fact, she'd claimed they were the reason she had ended up in bed with Rik. Which, considering her continued scorn about his emotions towards Dee, he found highly hypocritical!

It was a no-win situation as far as he could see, no matter how they continued to argue about it.

'How about we order some breakfast?' he suggested. 'That should be a safe topic of conversation, at least!'

'I'm not hungry,' Sapphie refused.

Neither was he. 'Then how about you and I go for a walk? You might work up an appetite,' he persevered.

'How about you and I...?' Sapphie gave a frustrated shake of her head. 'Haven't I got it through to you yet that I don't want to spend any more time in your company than I have to?'

Rik held on to his temper with effort. 'I believe you may have mentioned it once or twice.'

Her eyes flashed like molten gold. 'Then you have your answer, don't you?'

Rik held up the palms of his hands. 'I was only suggesting a walk, Sapphie, not a morning in bed together!'

She gasped, colour darkening her cheeks as she hastily looked about them to see if anyone was listening to their conversation.

They weren't; Rik had already checked. His only fun in this situation might be in teasing Sapphie, but he had no intention of causing her a moment's embarrassment in front of others. There was a certain dignity about her, a self-possession, that stopped him from ever doing that.

'Come on.' He stood up, moving to pull back her chair so that she had no choice but to stand up. 'A walk in the sunshine will do us both good.' It might also help to clear the cobwebs in his brain after his sleepless night. 'My intentions are strictly honourable, Sapphie,' he declared as she looked slightly dazed at finding herself outside the hotel and walking towards the River Seine and the looming Eiffel Tower.

She shot him a quick, disapproving glance, keeping

her distance as they progressed along the avenue. 'I've only ever been that stupid once in my life!'

Stupid? Was that how she thought of their night together? He had considered her his salvation at the time and whenever he had allowed himself to think of her afterwards it had always been with a smile of remembered affection.

And no matter what Sapphie might have felt, he *had* thought of her during the intervening years, had often wondered where she was, what she was doing, if she ever thought of him with the same affection.

Obviously not, if her horror at seeing him again yesterday was anything to go by!

'I never thought of you as stupid, Sapphie,' he assured her huskily. 'Although, having talked to you, I do understand your reasons a little better now—'

'You think I was a diversion to stop you from interfering with Dee's wedding,' she reminded hardly.

He winced at the accusation, knowing it was deserved, and regretting that he had ever said anything so hurtful. But he had been hurting himself yesterday and had hit out at the only person that he could. No excuse, he knew, but it was what had happened.

One thing he did know; her description of her engagement to Jerome, her love for him, had definitely rung true...

Rik squirmed uncomfortably. 'I might have been a little hasty when I made that remark—'

'Might have been!' she echoed. 'I was twenty-three years old, Rik, and although I had been engaged to marry Jerome, the two of us had never been lovers.

You were my first. Or were you too preoccupied that night with your own emotions to realise that?'

No, of course he hadn't been; that was an aspect of their night of passion that had always puzzled him. But, until just now, time and distance had convinced him that he must have imagined that small initial barrier to their lovemaking—that, of course, Sapphie couldn't have been a virgin. Anyway, women simply didn't give their virginity away to a complete stranger, did they?

Though Sapphie had…

CHAPTER FIVE

Too much!

After all her care yesterday, all her thinking before speaking, she had now said far too much…!

Admittedly he had just made her angry all over again with his doubts concerning her motivation five years ago, but even so, as she saw the sharp intelligence of his gaze, the questions starting to form there, she knew it had been a mistake to have let that anger provoke her into saying as much as she had.

As a virgin, the possibility of her using contraception that night had to have been nil, and Rik knew that he certainly hadn't used any. Damn her reckless tongue!

'But I wouldn't give that too much thought if I were you, Rik,' Sapphie dismissed brittlely. 'I've had dozens of lovers since, and I'm sure they were all grateful for the fact that you had already taken away that particular barrier!'

She knew by the angry darkening of his eyes that by pretending she'd slept with other men, she had successfully diverted his attention from the original subject; her virginity. Although, as his gaze now turned to Arctic grey, she wasn't too sure she would be able to handle his change of mood. But for both their sakes, as well as Matthew's—he was already fatherless, so it wouldn't do if his mother was throttled in the street too—she knew she had better try!

'Perhaps I was right about this walk not being a good idea,' she told him lightly as she came to a halt on the pavement. 'We don't seem to be able to be in each other's company for five minutes without one of us insulting the other!'

A nerve pulsed in his tightly clenched jaw as he obviously fought an inner battle to control his anger. 'Why is that, do you suppose?' he finally managed to rasp between clenched teeth.

'We simply don't like each other?' she suggested with a dismissive shrug.

Rik continued to glare at her for several long seconds, and then he seemed to force himself to relax, his hands unclenching at his sides, his mouth twisting into a humourless smile. 'But I do like you, Sapphie,' he mused. 'I find your forthright manner, the way you say exactly what you're thinking, very—refreshing.'

Sapphie's breath caught in her throat as her gaze was met and held by his now warm blue eyes.

'Perhaps it isn't that we dislike each other at all,' Rik continued gruffly, one hand reaching up to cup the side of her face, his fingers seeming to burn where they touched, holding her mesmerised. 'Perhaps it's that we like each other too much?' he murmured before his head lowered and his lips claimed hers.

She had realised yesterday how she still felt about this man, but it was an emotion she had denied by being continually rude and antagonistic towards him.

But now, with his lips gently exploring hers, she couldn't deny her feelings any longer. She loved this man. Unbelievable as it might seem, after five years' absence, she was still in love with Rik Prince!

Perhaps it was because of her deep love for Matthew, and his undeniable likeness to his father. Or perhaps she loved Matthew as much as she did because of that likeness to his father; whatever the reason, she knew, as her body instinctively melted into Rik's, that she was still in love with him!

The summer sun beat down on them hotly, but Sapphie's heat was all coming from inside, making it impossible for her to think; she was only capable of feeling.

And what she felt was remembered desire; her hands clung to the broad width of Rik's shoulders, her body curved into his, making her completely aware of his own arousal.

'Well, well, well,' drawled a self-satisfied male voice. 'And you told me I was wasting my time, Dee, trying to get Sapphie and Rik together!'

Sapphie and Rik had sprung guiltily apart at the sound of Jerome's voice, Sapphie now shooting Dee a wary glance at Jerome's comment.

As Sapphie had suspected, Jerome was trying to throw her and Rik together, and from the furious expression on Dee's face—her eyes were sparkling a venomous emerald—her sister was far from pleased that he seemed to have succeeded.

Not that he had. Sapphie might still love Rik, respond to him as she had to no other man, but it would be an act of madness on her part to even contemplate becoming involved with him again. Dee's obvious displeasure, at the mere idea of Rik and Sapphie liking each other, had nothing to do with it!

As for Rik, Sapphie couldn't even look at him at the moment, didn't trust herself not to give away her feelings. Neither did she want to witness the apologetic expression that was sure to be on his face as he looked to Dee for forgiveness for what had, after all, only been an impulse on his part!

'Actually, Jerome,' Sapphie briskly took charge of the situation, 'Rik and I were just saying goodbye to each other; I've decided to return to England on the Eurostar train with the two of you this afternoon.' The idea had only just occurred to her, but the more she thought about it the more she liked the idea of going home. Safely away from the temptation of Rik Prince!

'That sounds like an excellent idea,' Dee grated, obviously only slightly mollified by this news. 'I'm sure that Matthew will be eagerly awaiting your return,' she added challengingly.

Sapphie felt her heart miss a beat, her face go pale, at Dee's deliberate mention of her young son. Had Dee somehow realised? Did she know why Sapphie had steadfastly refused to share with anyone all these years the identity of Matthew's father? It was what Sapphie had feared ever since meeting Rik again yesterday, the reason she had endured the dinner together last night; she simply couldn't let Dee or Jerome tell Rik that she had a young son.

No, Sapphie decided after a searching glance at her sister; Dee was angry at what she saw as this current defection of her ex-lover, rather than venting her fury at how quickly her ex-lover had turned to Sapphie for consolation five years ago and shared an unforgettable night of passion.

And it had been unforgettable. As far as Sapphie was concerned, at least.

She had always thought, following Matthew's birth, that it was her concentration on him that had robbed her of any desire to become involved with another man. Now she knew that wasn't the case at all...

Because, despite what she might have told Rik a short time ago in self-defence, she had only ever had one lover in her life—and that was Rik.

'Matthew?' Rik queried abruptly, a slight edge to his voice.

If Sapphie had needed any confirmation that Dee was still completely ignorant of the identity of Matthew's father, then she got it now. Her sister's expression was blazingly triumphant as she sensed Sapphie's discomfort with the subject. Besides, Sapphie acknowledged, if Dee had once realised that Rik was Matthew's father, then she certainly wouldn't want Rik to know about it now. Dee was out to make trouble, yes, but not the amount that would erupt if Rik were to discover he and Sapphie had a son! Rik's attention would be totally focused on Sapphie then!

Dee stepped forward, giving Rik a teasing smile as she linked her arm with his. 'Now, now, Rik, we women have to have our little secrets, you know,' she murmured suggestively.

Jerome frowned. 'I don't see what the big deal is. It's not as if Sapphie—'

'Darling, if Sapphie hasn't told Rik about Matthew,

then we really shouldn't do so, either.' Dee gave her husband a coquettish smile, still clinging to Rik's arm, glowingly lovely in a short cotton dress that exactly matched the colour of her eyes and showed off the long length of her tanned legs. 'Although I do think it's naughty of you not to have mentioned him, Sapphie,' she admonished.

Sapphie turned in Rik's direction, only to find him staring straight back at her with hooded blue eyes, that gave her absolutely no insight as to what he was thinking, either about the kiss the two of them had shared or the conversation since Dee and Jerome had joined them.

She quickly averted her gaze, her own emotions in turmoil; just looking at Dee's proprietorial claim on him upset her, not to mention how close Rik had come to learning that she had a young son.

He wasn't stupid—far from it, could count as well as she could, and Matthew's age of four years and two months, plus the nine months of her pregnancy, would take him exactly to the point the two of them had last met!

'As you say, Dee,' she muttered stiffly, 'we women must have our little secrets.'

Dee smiled, looking like a cat who had got the cream, obviously completely satisfied with the way this conversation was turning out. 'The waiter said the two of you had left without eating; shall we all go back to the hotel and have breakfast together?' she suggested brightly.

Sapphie couldn't think of food at this moment, knew that it would choke her. She couldn't even look at Rik right now, let alone sit and eat a meal with him as if nothing had happened.

But maybe it hadn't for him; after all, he wasn't still in love with her, neither did he have the secret of their son to guard with all the fierceness of a lioness protecting her cub!

'Actually, I think I'll just go back to my hotel and check the availability of seats on the Eurostar,' she answered evasively, having no intention of being left alone in Paris with Rik once the other couple had left, and feeling too disturbed at this moment to even try to monitor the conversation between Rik and the other two. 'I need to pack as well.'

'If none of you have any objections, I think I might travel to England with you, too,' Rik put in mildly.

Unbelievably.

Devastatingly!

Sapphie had thought she'd hit on the perfect way to avoid seeing Rik ever again, and instead it seemed she was to be stuck on a train back to London with him, and Dee and Jerome, for several hours.

It had to be her idea of purgatory!

It was impossible for him to mistake the look of absolute dismay on Sapphie's face at his suggestion!

Rik wasn't quite sure where the idea had come from. He'd intended returning to the States from here, rather than going to England. But, now he'd come up with the idea, it seemed the right thing to do.

Having believed himself in love with Dee for the last five years, and then discovering that wasn't the case at all, he now found himself drawn to Sapphie.

Whether it was because of their past association, or because she was the first woman he had been in close contact with since his startling realisation, he really wasn't sure yet. But he was very attracted to her and he wasn't comfortable letting her just disappear out of his life for a second time.

If the sense of jealousy that had shot through him at the mere mention of this guy Matthew's presence in her life was anything to go by, then he was right to pursue this attraction, and not just walk away. He had already done that once where Dee was concerned, and he knew he had been correct to do so. Sapphie wore no rings on her left hand, so this Matthew wasn't her husband or fiancé. In fact, if the man was anyone really important in her life, he would be with her in Paris right now, wouldn't he? What was that saying? *'All's fair in love and war'…?*

Well, he seemed to have been fighting a continuous battle with Sapphie ever since the two of them met again yesterday!

As for how he felt about her—he didn't quite know yet; he just had this feeling of unfinished business between them. And he wasn't going to spend another five years of his life wondering about what might have been!

He was totally aware of Sapphie, had in his possession an elusive memory of her lithe nakedness moving against his, of her legs wrapped about him, of her little cries of pleasure as he kissed and caressed her, of tiny teeth sinking into his shoulder as their pleasure reached its peak…

No, he wasn't yet willing to let Sapphie walk out of his life a second time.

'I think I'll give breakfast a miss too,' he told Dee and Jerome lightly. 'In fact—' he extricated himself from Dee's arm linked with his '—why don't Sapphie and I meet up with the two of you again later? Say, twelvish?'

Dee looked far from pleased at the way he had moved away from her and closer to Sapphie, her expression tight as she looked at both of them from beneath lowered lashes.

'Sounds good to me,' Jerome was the one to answer Rik smilingly. 'Come on, honey; I'm starving!' He smiled encouragingly at his wife.

'Well, I'm not,' Dee snapped uncooperatively.

To give Jerome his due, his smile didn't so much as waver for a second, whereas Rik knew that if his wife ever spoke to him in that petulant tone in front of other people he would be far from pleased.

His wife?

That was a joke; the only woman he had ever asked to be his wife was this other man's wife!

But even so, if Dee had ever spoken to him like that— What was he doing? Dee had always been perfect in his eyes, the woman he measured every other female against. And had always found them wanting.

But, he realised begrudgingly, the last twenty-four hours in Dee's company, the discrepancies he had found in what she'd told him and wondering what was actually fact and what was fiction, had made him question just how well he had actually known Dee all those years ago. They had really only been out on a few dates together before she'd told him of her impending marriage to Jerome, and the reasons for it. At which point Rik had decided he wanted to marry her himself, that he couldn't live without her.

And yet he had. Quite successfully, on a professional level. It might not have been quite so successful from a personal point of view, but even that side of his life had had its moments.

Of course, Sapphie had been one of its highlights…!

'You must be hungry, Dee,' Jerome told his wife firmly. 'I know you didn't feel too well this morning, but that's passed now. You're just feeling cranky because of your condition.'

Condition? What condition? Was Dee ill—?

No, Rik realised with a sudden intake of breath, Dee wasn't ill at all—she was pregnant!

Why was he so surprised? The other couple had been married five years now, a family was a natural progression, wasn't it?

And did he really care, or was it just force of habit that made him react…?

'Yes, do go and have some breakfast with Jerome, Dee,' Sapphie was the one to put in lightly, at the same time stepping forward to link her arm with Rik's.

He looked down at her frowningly, the force of the anger sparkling in her amber-coloured eyes was enough to make his own widen.

Idiot, her gaze scorned, why don't you just get a grip and stop making an idiot of yourself over Dee?

He straightened abruptly, not sure that was what he was doing. It was a bit of a shock to learn of the pregnancy, yes, but, there again, it wasn't really any of his business, was it?

'Yes, do go ahead, Dee,' he encouraged lightly. 'After all, you're eating for two now!' he offered, receiving a venomous look from her glittering green eyes for his trouble.

Really, these two sisters certainly knew how to let a man know exactly what they were thinking without saying a word! Sapphie was patently furious with him, and Dee was far from happy too—though, as far as he was aware, he was doing his best to keep things on a friendly basis with everyone.

Even if it was hard going!

It was his own fault, of course. He had put Dee on a pedestal, believing her to be perfect, that he could never love anyone else in the way that he loved her. How stupid was that, based on a few days of knowing each other? Especially as she had then told him she was about to marry another man!

Very, he acknowledged with a self-derisive wince. No wonder Sapphie made no effort to hide her scorn every time she looked at him!

Sapphie.

Surprisingly, he felt he knew her so much better than he had ever known Dee, personally as well as physically. The physical part was a fact, but the personal part was there every time she spoke to him in that bluntly truthful way of hers, every time she looked at him with those frankly assessing eyes.

And found him wanting…

Justifiably so, he acknowledged heavily. He had been an idiot to believe himself in love with a mirage for five years…!

'Don't be ridiculous, Rik,' Dee told him sharply. 'The baby is minute. No one looking at me would even know I'm pregnant!'

He certainly hadn't, Rik allowed. Dee had looked just the same to him when they met again yesterday, perhaps even more glowingly beautiful than he remembered. But then his sister, Stazy, had had an added glow about her when she was pregnant with Sam, so perhaps that was normal. His knowledge of pregnant women was limited. Obviously.

'You see? Cranky,' Jerome murmured indulgently as he put his arm about his wife's shoulders and turned her back in the direction of the hotel. 'We'll see you two later,' he added before leading away a disgruntled Dee.

Leaving an awkward silence in their wake as Rik, at this moment, couldn't think of a thing to say, and Sapphie—well, she was probably still disgusted with him!

'You didn't know, did you?'

He turned to look enquiringly at Sapphie as she spoke to him.

'You didn't know about the baby until just now, did you?' she persisted evenly.

He frowned. 'Why should I have known?'

'No reason. I just thought—'

'Don't bother to tell me what you thought,' Rik responded swiftly. Then his tone softened. 'I...It was kind of you to—help me out of what could have been an awkward situation.'

Her eyes flashed deeply gold. 'I didn't do it for you, I did it for Jerome. He's so excited about the baby.'

Rik nodded. 'And how does Dee feel about it?'

Sapphie gave him a cold look. 'You would have to ask her that, not me.'

'Look, Sapphie,' he rasped, beginning to feel angry all over again, 'no matter what you may think to the contrary, I really hadn't seen Dee since her wedding and we met again by chance yesterday outside Fouquet's. A fact I'm sure I've already told you more than once. And again, despite what you may think, I do not tell lies,' he added harshly.

'But how can you possibly have continued to be in love with someone you haven't even spoken to for five years…?' She broke off quickly, colour heightening her cheeks now. 'Forget I asked that,' she muttered dismissively. 'It's none of my business what you do.' She turned away. 'I really should get back to my hotel, check on the train and pack. If you'll excuse me?' She didn't wait for him to answer before hurrying off in the direction of her hotel.

Rik watched her go, the sunlight making her hair a deep red halo of colour, her body swaying tantalisingly as she walked.

Away from him.

Leaving him with the distinct feeling that Sapphie Benedict had no time for him, or what she considered his confused emotions.

Except they were no longer that confused to Rik. He had been in love with the mirage that was his vision of Dee.

Now he wasn't.

He wasn't sure what he felt for Sapphie yet.

But he did feel something!

CHAPTER SIX

WHAT on earth had possessed her to get into a conversation with Rik about his feelings for Dee?

If she had managed to be in love with Rik for the last five years without seeing or speaking to him, then why did she think it was ludicrous that he had felt the same about Dee?

Admittedly, she did have a day-to-day reminder of Rik in Matthew; tangible proof of that one night they had spent together. But even so, she should have got over her feelings for Rik long ago.

She certainly shouldn't have allowed him to kiss her—or have kissed him back—this morning.

Or have let Dee witness that kiss...

Because she was sure, as far as her possessive younger sister was concerned, she hadn't heard the last about that!

Sapphie was proved right, it turned out—she hadn't heard the last of it. Dee took the first available opportunity to talk to her about it, that very afternoon. Rik and Jerome had gone off in search of coffee for them all before they boarded the Eurostar train, leaving Sapphie and Dee seated together in a quiet corner of the departure lounge.

'Exactly what did you think you were doing, Sapphie?' Dee demanded, green eyes glittering angrily. 'Rik is mine, you know, and he always will be,' she proclaimed with confidence.

It really wasn't Dee's fault she was so utterly self-ish, Sapphie reminded herself patiently. Dee had been petted and spoilt by their family from the moment she was born; her father had adored her because, to him, Dee was perfection personified; her mother had in-dulged her because she was pleased to have a child with her second husband; Sapphie had been delighted to have a little sister to play with.

Which had all been fine when Dee was a little girl, but as she matured, and everything became 'mine', it had become less attractive. Dee continued to demand, and usually get, adoration from everyone she met. Even her career had fulfilled that demand, the public flocking to see every film she'd starred in—indeed, several people had already stopped her today to ask her for her autograph! Only her warmth and beauty were on show to her public, Jerome having so far managed to keep her temper tantrums, when she couldn't have her own way, from the Press.

But she was going too far when she put people under the heading of 'mine'—even if Rik Prince did give every impression of fitting that pigeon-hole!

'No one is disputing your prior claim to a friend-ship with Rik, Dee,' Sapphie answered soothingly, although she suspected that Jerome might have some-thing to say about that!

Dee raised blonde brows. 'It was much more than a friendship!'

Sapphie knew it was, didn't doubt for a moment

that Dee and Rik had once been lovers. She just didn't want to hear about it!

'Fine,' she replied uninterestedly.

'It is not "fine",' Dee snapped. 'The two of you were kissing earlier. And now he's decided to travel to England, instead of back to the States as he originally planned to do!'

'I really don't think the two incidents are related, Dee,' Sapphie responded wearily; she had no idea why Rik had changed his plans, but one thing she did know: it had absolutely nothing to do with her! 'I explained earlier about the kiss,' she continued evenly. 'And if Rik has changed his plans, then it probably has more to do with you than it does with me.'

'Do you think so?' Dee brightened.

Even at twenty-five, and expecting a child of her own, her little sister could still be so immature. 'I do. I also—thank you for not telling him about Matthew earlier,' Sapphie added quietly, still very aware of the narrow escape she'd had.

Dee gave her a feline glance. 'That doesn't mean I'm not going to,' she purred. 'It's just that Rik can be so—shall we say?—indulgent towards women, and I didn't want you coming on to him as some poor, pathetic, single-mother figure!'

Sapphie bit her bottom lip to stop herself from laughing; poor, pathetic, single-mother figure be damned! There was nothing poor or pathetic about her. She earned more than enough money to keep herself and Matthew very comfortably and, although she didn't go out that often, she still had plenty of friends she could see if she wanted to. But it would serve no positive purpose to point this out to Dee, who only ever saw what she wanted to see. At the moment she was making it very plain that she didn't want to see Sapphie anywhere near Rik!

Which was perfectly OK with Sapphie; once they reached London later today, she didn't want to be anywhere near Rik either!

Although it was a little difficult to avoid him once they were in the close confines of their train carriage!

Their first-class seats were the height of comfort, and the stewardess was very attentive. But the four of them were seated around a small table, two facing forwards and two backwards, and as Jerome wouldn't hear of anyone sitting next to Dee besides himself, that left Sapphie and Rik sitting next to each other, too.

Not that Dee had too much time to voice any objections to the arrangement. She fell asleep shortly after they left Paris, Jerome quickly joining her in slumber as he rested his dark head on her golden one.

The first few months of pregnancy could be extremely tiring, as Sapphie well knew, the body having to adjust to all sorts of changes. It had been a bout of morning sickness earlier today that had prevented Dee and Jerome joining them for breakfast, as planned.

'What were you researching in Paris?'

She turned back to look at Rik as his soft voice questioned her.

'Sorry?'

He turned to face her, his broad shoulders moving

beneath the black jacket he wore over a white T-shirt and faded denims. 'You mentioned yesterday that you were in Paris doing some research…?'

Yesterday? Was it really only twenty-four hours since her world had been turned upside down? Life was never going to be quite the same again after this chance meeting with Rik. Because it could happen again at any time, just as it had this time, when she least expected it!

'Once I moved back to England—'

'You left your job as Jerome's PA?'

She smiled. 'I was persuaded, shall we say, that it wasn't quite the thing to do. In the circumstances.'

'I see,' Rik murmured, glancing across at the sleeping Dee with narrowed eyes. 'So you not only lost your fiancé, but your job too?' There was a steely edge to his voice now.

'It was the best move I ever made,' Sapphie responded quickly; she was not about to give him a condensed version of all Dee's little faults and foibles. 'I became a freelance interviewer, doing profiles on the rich and famous, stuff like that. But truth really can be stranger than fiction, and some of the things I learnt…!' She laughed softly. 'I've just managed to have my first book published. And to answer your question, I was in Paris researching part of my second book.'

'You're a writer?' Rik looked impressed. 'What sort of—? Wait a minute!' He sat up straighter in his seat. 'You wouldn't happen to be the new thriller writer everyone is raving about—S.P. Benedict, the author of *Cold Night*—would you?'

Her mouth quirked. 'Sapphire Pearl Benedict,' she announced with feeling. 'A bit of a mouthful, don't you think? Although thank you for at least having heard of my book.'

'It's worse than that, I'm afraid, Sapphie—I've read it!' he told her teasingly. 'My brother, Nik, gave it to me. At one point he was thinking of trying to acquire the film rights, but I read it and...' He broke off. 'You know, Sapphie,' he continued, 'just for once, I would like the two of us to have a conversation without one of us insulting the other!'

Sapphie couldn't help her burst of laughter at the totally awkward expression on Rik's face, although she quietened it down to a soft chuckle as she saw they were disturbing the other couple. 'Perhaps it would be better if we didn't talk at all,' she suggested.

'Not an option,' Rik told her firmly. 'Why don't we just move over there?' He indicated the empty seats opposite them; the carriage was actually only half full. 'Then we won't be disturbing anyone.'

Oh, no? Sapphie was disturbed every moment she spent in this man's company!

Although she found it wasn't quite as bad sitting at the table opposite Rik, who was facing her now rather than sitting next to her, his denim-clad knee occasionally touching hers.

'So you're an author,' Rik said again admiringly. 'It seems we have more in common that I realised.'

'Not really,' Sapphie instantly denied, not wanting to get drawn into that trap. 'Although working with all those actors and actresses, you must be able to appreciate how easy it would be for one of them to murder the other!' she said lightly, hoping to lead the conversation off on another tack.

He pulled a face. 'As a lowly screenwriter, I'm more likely to be the victim than the murderer!'

There was nothing in the least lowly about Rik Prince's writing. He more often than not worked alongside his brothers, Nik Prince, the director, and Zak Prince, the actor. But he didn't collaborate with them exclusively, having worked with and for all the top Hollywood directors at one time or another.

She was hardly on his level, with only one book to her credit!

'Maybe I should make that the subject of my next book,' she said sharply. 'Screenwriter murdered with his own pen!'

'I use a laptop,' Rik drawled drily, at the same time indicating the slim leather case he had placed in the overhead rack opposite.

'Even better,' Sapphie retaliated. 'It would make a rather good blunt instrument, and I bet all the blood could easily be washed off afterwards too.'

Rik gave a rueful smile. 'Vicious little thing, aren't you?'

'I believe I could be,' she acknowledged. 'Given the right circumstances.' Such as someone trying to take her son away from her!

She was sure that most mothers must feel this way, that well of fierce protective maternal love driving them from the minute it swept over them when their newborn child was placed in their arms. Sapphie knew it drove her, and it was a feeling that hadn't diminished in the slightest the last four years. In fact, it had probably grown stronger!

Which was why one part of her—the part that still loved him—wanted to be closer to Rik, while the other part of her—the part that knew how dangerous he was to her son's future—wanted to keep him at arm's length. If not further. Much further!

'But let's not talk about me,' she dismissed briskly. 'You mentioned that you've been working while you were in Paris…?'

'Writing the adapted screenplay for *No Ordinary Boy*,' he explained. 'A labour of love rather than work. My brother, Nik, recently married Jinx Nixon; she's related to the author of the book.'

'I saw their photograph in the newspapers,' Sapphie recalled, also remembering that moment of panic she had felt at the time when she'd realised how much alike the eldest and youngest Prince brothers were, both of them dark and steely-eyed. 'They looked very happy together.'

'They are,' Rik agreed. 'I never thought I would see my big brother fall in love, but boy, when he did…!' He gave an affectionate shake of his head.

'I met him once,' Sapphie explained. 'It was when I was working for Jerome,' she elaborated at Rik's questioning glance. 'I remember Nik as being one of the most focused people I had ever met.'

'He still is,' Rik affirmed. 'But now he's focused on Jinx rather than anything else.'

'Lucky Jinx,' Sapphie murmured wistfully.

Rik looked at her searchingly. 'You aren't another

one of the legion of women who've fallen for my big brother's arrogant elusiveness, are you?'

'Certainly not,' she was stung into replying. 'I admired his attitude to his work.' Her cheeks became flushed. 'Anyway, I'm sure that's all changed now that he's married.'

'Jinx doesn't seem to have any complaints,' Rik agreed.

'Maybe she's already learnt not to,' Sapphie came back tartly. 'I certainly have no intention of ever becoming some man's possession.' She really had no idea whether or not Jinx and Nik's marriage was like that, her remark meant on a personal basis rather than as a criticism of their relationship.

She was her own person, and intended remaining that way. For Matthew's sake as well as her own.

'I don't think that's quite how it is with Nik and Jinx,' Rik rebuked her lightly. 'Jinx is far too strong a character to be dominated in that way. For instance, Nik is the one who has moved to England, shifting the base of Prince Movies to there. Jinx's work is in the UK, and so is her father. Who, incidentally, lives with them.' Having declared his love for Jinx, Nik's commitment had been total.

That sort of loving was obviously a family trait, Rik recognised—except that he had been in love with totally the wrong woman for the last five years!

No, perhaps that was being a little hard on himself. Until yesterday, the woman he'd loved had had Dee's face and body. But after another twenty-four hours spent in her company, he'd come to know that the woman he had loved wasn't real at all.

The woman he'd thought he loved had fire tempered with vulnerability, valued honesty above everything else. Dee wasn't that woman. She had lied to him about so much five years ago—about her family, as well as her reasons for marrying Jerome; so how could he now believe a single word she said?

It was going to take some adjusting to, but he knew with certainty that he really wasn't in love with Dee any more. If he ever really had been...

'You don't have to defend your brother to me, Rik,' Sapphie assured him. 'My opinion of him is totally irrelevant. I met Nik once; I'm unlikely to meet him again.'

Rik tensed. 'How can you be so sure about that?'

'Because people like the Prince brothers have no part in my day-to-day life.'

In other words, he wasn't going to have any part in her day-to-day life, then, either. Not that Sapphie had made any secret of the fact that she wasn't pleased to see him again after all this time. But still it hurt to be dismissed by her in this casual way.

'I'm a Prince brother, and I seem to be part of your life at this moment,' he pointed out mildly.

She gave a nervous smile. 'Once we reach London, and have gone our separate ways, I doubt there will be any reason for the two of us to ever meet again.'

Her tone implied that couldn't happen soon enough, as far as she was concerned. Which irritated Rik intensely!

'I was hoping that you might have dinner with me this evening?' he offered challengingly.

Sapphie gave him a startled look, too surprised to

even try to hide her reaction. 'Why on earth would you want me to do that?' she said incredulously. 'More to the point,' she went on, 'why on earth would you think I would want to have dinner with you, this evening or any other time?' She looked totally stunned by the suggestion.

Rik felt himself scowling darkly. 'Look, I know I behaved badly five years ago, Sapphie—'

'I would rather not talk about that, if you don't mind!' she hissed forcefully, before shooting a pointed look in the direction of the still dozing Dee and Jerome.

Rik sat forward to lean across the table towards her, keeping his voice to a whisper. 'I don't agree. I think we should discuss it,' his tone levelled reasonably, 'if only to set the record straight between us.'

'There's nothing to set straight between us!' Sapphie shot back at him fiercely. 'And I'm sure you don't usually return to discuss one-night stands after they've happened!'

He drew in an angry breath. 'I have never thought of that night in those terms—'

'Of course you have!' she ripped back. 'Stop trying to romanticise something that just wasn't that way at all!'

Perhaps he had been guilty of thinking of their night together in those terms, but he didn't think of it that way now any more—and he didn't care for the fact that she still did!

'That night was as much out of character for me as I'm sure it was for you,' he grated. 'Ask anyone who knows me: my brothers, my sister, and they will all tell you—'

'I have no intention of discussing that night with any third party, thank you very much!' she told him, drawing in controlling breaths. When she spoke again, her voice had softened and become reasoning. 'Why can't you just accept that I want to forget that night? That it would be better for everyone if you did, too?'

He sighed his frustration at her stubbornness. 'I want to get to know you better, Sapphie—'

'Well, I don't want to know another single thing about you,' she assured him. 'Now, would you just leave the subject alone?' she demanded with feeling as she observed Dee and Jerome beginning to wake up.

No, he was afraid he couldn't do that. Not now that he had met Sapphie again. Because she was much more real to him, their night together was so much more real to him, than the mirage of Dee he had carried around in his heart for five years.

But, in the circumstances, he knew that convincing Sapphie of that was going to be no easy task!

Still, a Prince had never been one to back away from a challenge...

Although none of his plans to see Sapphie again showed in his demeanour for the rest of the train journey as he conversed lightly with Dee and Jerome.

Only Sapphie remained distant and apart from the conversation. No doubt wishing the miles away so that she could get away from him all the sooner!

Was there something wrong with him, he wondered, some quirk in his nature that made him feel attracted to women who didn't want to know? Well…in Dee's case, that wasn't strictly true; she had given him the impression that she wanted him too, but couldn't have him. Sapphie just didn't want him!

Except that he was pretty sure he hadn't mistaken her response this morning when he'd kissed her…

He was also pretty sure that he wanted to kiss her again. And sooner, rather than later!

'I have a car waiting, if you would like to join us?' Jerome informed Sapphie and Rik, as they all made their way out of Waterloo Station. Other bystanders started recognizing Dee, and soon a crowd had started to gather around them.

'No, thanks, I think we'll just take a cab.' Rik was the one to answer for both himself and Sapphie, at the same time as he took a proprietorial hold of her arm.

'I'll see you later this evening, Sapphie, when I visit Mummy,' Dee had time to call out to her sister before she and Jerome were caught up in the crowd and their wave of adoration for the actress, Diamond McCall.

'Phew.' Rik breathed his relief as he and Sapphie escaped the throng.

Sapphie pulled out of his grasp before stepping away from him. 'I'm not getting in any taxi with you,' she told him stiffly, seeming even more distant now that they were back on her native soil.

He wasn't too surprised at having his plan to take Sapphie home thwarted, and at the same time find out her address; Sapphie was neither stupid, nor gullible.

Of course, there was always the possibility that she shared a home with the faceless Matthew…

Damn it, why hadn't he thought of that earlier?

'I wasn't seriously suggesting that you would,' he rasped harshly, more annoyed than he could ever have imagined he'd be at the idea of Sapphie living with another man. 'I just thought you would prefer not to be caught up in Dee's three-ring circus!'

Mobile phones and cameras were flashing further down the station now, as excited travellers took their chance to record the actress's arrival. There were even one or two paparazzi.

With a cynicism Rik hadn't known he possessed, he couldn't help wondering if Dee or Jerome hadn't tipped off the Press themselves. Dee certainly seemed to court adoration, and Jerome, as her agent, was too much of a businessman not to want to take advantage of that.

'Oh.' Sapphie looked slightly nonplussed at his explanation. 'I would.' She smiled awkwardly. 'Thank you.'

Rik felt his anger fading. 'Did it hurt you to say that?'

She gave a self-deriding grimace. 'Only a little,' she sighed before drawing herself up determinedly and thrusting out her hand. 'Well, Rik, this is goodbye. It's been—interesting, meeting you again.' She gave a humourless smile. 'Perhaps we can do it again in another five years or so!'

Rik reached out to lightly grasp the hand she held out to him, not to shake as she had intended, but to gently pull her towards him. 'This isn't goodbye,

Sapphie,' he warned, unable to fight the compulsion he felt to take her in his arms and kiss her.

And for a moment—too brief a moment as far as he was concerned!—he felt her response, her lips parting beneath his, the slenderness of her body pressed against his, her breasts warm and soft—

Sapphie pulled sharply away, her eyes blazing like molten gold as she glared up at him. 'I said goodbye, Rik, and that was what I meant!' She bent to pick up her bag before turning on her heel and walking away from him, quickly becoming lost in the crowd.

Rik stood where she left him, not even attempting to stop or follow her, knowing he had pushed his luck enough for one day where Sapphie was concerned.

He walked slowly out of the station, got into a cab and gave the driver his brother Nik's address, a slight smile starting to curve his lips as he settled back on the seat and began to formulate a plan for seeing Sapphie again.

Because no matter what Sapphie might think to the contrary—might hope to the contrary!—there was far too much left unsaid and done between them for him to allow this to be the last they saw of each other.

Far too much!

CHAPTER SEVEN

'HONESTLY, Mother, I have absolutely no idea what we're even doing here!' Sapphie grumbled as she looked around the star-filled reception room in one of London's top hotels.

'Don't be such a wet blanket, Sapphie,' Joan McCall chided her daughter affectionately. Joan was still a voluptuously attractive woman in her early fifties, the black sequinned dress she was wearing showing off her curvaceous figure to advantage, her shoulder-length auburn hair only needing a little professional help to maintain that vibrant colour. 'I, for one, am enjoying myself. This is the first time Dee has ever invited us to one of these parties.' Joan glowed happily.

Actually, technically, Dee hadn't done the inviting this time; Jerome had. And after a week of glancing nervously over her shoulder in case Rik should suddenly appear—there had been far too much of a determined glint in his eyes when they'd parted a week ago for her to be sure that he wouldn't!—Sapphie was treating the whole thing with suspicion. But so far— thank goodness!—there wasn't a Prince in sight!

And there was no doubting that her mother was enjoying this after-première party. They hadn't actually been invited to see the film itself—but Joan's face lit up excitedly as her hazel-coloured eyes spotted one star after another.

Sapphie, less trusting of the sudden invitation, had checked, and double-checked, to see if any of the Prince brothers—director, actor, or screenwriter—had had anything to do with the making of Dee's latest film. They hadn't. So, reluctantly, and under pressure from her mother, Sapphie had accepted for both of them.

She sipped her glass of champagne and looked around her—there had to be some consolation to feeling like a goldfish in the midst of a group of piranhas!—before answering her mother. 'Personally, I would much rather be at home with Matthew,' she muttered, not at all mollified by the fact that Matthew had told her she looked a lovely mummy when she went to tuck him in and kiss him goodnight.

To add insult to injury, she had even had to go out and buy a new dress for the evening! Occasionally Sapphie went to parties, or enjoyed just quiet evenings with friends. But there had certainly been nothing in her wardrobe to wear to a post-première party. Especially one that celebrated her sister as the star of the film!

Her mother had gone on the dress-shopping expedition with her, persuading Sapphie to spend some of her hard-earned royalties on a Chinese-style sheath of gold-coloured silk. With her hair lightly secured on top of her head, her legs tanned and silky and three-inch heels on her gold-coloured shoes, Dee certainly couldn't complain that she hadn't made an effort!

'Don't be silly, dear,' her mother dismissed distractedly now. 'It's eleven o'clock; Matthew has been asleep for hours.'

'Curled up in bed with a good book, then,' Sapphie persisted; who on earth went out to a party that only started at ten-thirty?

She would stay for an hour, an hour and a half at the outside, she had promised herself when she accepted the invitation. Just long enough to add weight to the happy-family image that Dee was promoting this week.

The news of Dee's pregnancy had appeared in the newspapers earlier in the week, photographs of an ecstatic Dee and Jerome printed along with them.

Although as she looked at Dee now, surrounded by friends and admirers, radiantly beautiful in a revealing green dress that exactly matched the colour of her eyes, her figure still slender and willowy, it was difficult to believe that in six months' time she would be a mother.

Sapphie shook her head as she turned back to her starry-eyed mother. 'I can't wait to leave!'

'I'm sorry to hear that, Miss Benedict,' a man drawled pleasantly behind her, his accent noticeably American—although thankfully it wasn't Rik Prince's! 'It is Miss Benedict, isn't it?' the man enquired lightly as Sapphie turned sharply. 'I believe we met in New York several years ago.'

The man was older than Rik, his eyes a cool grey, but nevertheless the likeness between the two men was obvious; the dark hair was the same, as was the powerfully lean body, and that sensually smiling mouth.

Nik Prince!

There was no mistaking those arrogantly sculptured features. And if Sapphie had any doubts—which she didn't!—the red-haired woman standing smilingly beside him gave his identity away; it was only weeks ago that a blaze of publicity had surrounded Juliet 'Jinx' Nixon, now Jinx Prince, and her photograph had been on the front page of every British newspaper.

Sapphie had met Nik Prince only briefly six years ago, and she very much doubted she was memorable enough for this man to greet her again like this. But the alternative of Rik having talked to his eldest brother about her didn't ring true either.

'Yes, we did,' Sapphie finally answered him politely.

'I thought I recognised you.'

Sapphie still wasn't convinced. 'This is my mother, Joan McCall.' She drew her mother forward into the circle. 'This is Nik and Juliet Prince, Mother,' she introduced guardedly, still wary at having Nik Prince's considerable charm turned on her.

A charm which he now turned on her mother. 'I can see why Sapphie and Dee are so beautiful; obviously they both take after their lovely mother!' he complimented Joan warmly as the two shook hands. 'You don't look old enough to be an almost-grandmother!'

Joan blushed with pleasure at this flattery from

such a gorgeously handsome man. 'How kind of you to say so, Mr Prince, but actually I'm al—'

'Mr Prince is a well-known film director, Mother,' Sapphie quickly cut in over what she was sure was going to be a mention of Joan's other grandchild, Matthew. Sapphie's son.

'Please call me Nik,' he invited. 'And most of my wife's intimate friends call her Jinx,' he went on warmly, the smile he bestowed on his wife one of intimacy.

Which was a good enough reason for Sapphie to stick to calling the other woman Juliet; she wasn't going to become intimate with any of the Prince family!

'I find these parties a little overwhelming too,' Juliet confided, clearly attuned to Sapphie's own discomfort. 'Perhaps when Rik arrives we can all go and have a quiet drink somewhere else in the hotel?'

Only one part of that suggestion registered with Sapphie—*when Rik arrives*!

She glanced quickly around the room, feeling like prey that was being hunted, but unsure exactly which direction the attack was going to come from!

Rik was coming to this party, too!

Now she was convinced that her invitation wasn't just the act of kindness on Jerome's part that it had appeared. But the question was, who had been instrumental in setting this meeting up: Jerome, as another act of misguided matchmaking, or Rik himself?

The fact that Nik Prince and his wife were here and

had made a point of coming over and speaking to her made her inclined to believe it was the latter...

But why? Hadn't she made it more than obvious—bluntly so!—that she didn't want to see Rik again?

And hadn't she also spent the last week just waiting for something like this to happen, convinced that Rik had meant it when he told her it wasn't goodbye?

She drew in a deeply controlling breath, her smile forced as she turned back to look at the Princes, her hand tightly clutching her evening bag. 'That won't be possible, I'm afraid,' she declined evenly, while inside her feelings were in turmoil; she had to get away from here before Rik arrived! 'I have to be home by twelve o'clock.' Thank goodness she had only booked the babysitter until then!

'Why is that?' drawled an all-too-familiar voice. 'Do you turn into a pumpkin at midnight?'

Sapphie froze, having been surreptitiously watching the main doors for Rik's entrance. However, it seemed he had chosen instead to enter by one of the fire exits at the back of the room. He couldn't have chosen a better way to disconcert her!

Well, if that had been his intention, he had definitely succeeded!

Actually, disconcerted didn't even begin to describe how she felt as she slowly turned to face him, her breath completely taken away by how gorgeous he looked in a black dinner suit, black bow-tie and snowy white shirt, his hair slightly damp, as if it was raining outside, or he had recently taken a shower.

His warm blue eyes echoed the companionship

he'd offered her on the train from Paris, his smile wide with pleasure as he took hold of her hand before bending to kiss her lightly on the cheeks. 'It's good to see you again,' he told her quietly, at the same time keeping a firm hold of her hand.

Everything else apart—her mother's presence, Rik's brother and sister-in-law, Matthew—she had to admit it was good to see him too. Her pulse fluttered erratically and her cheeks grew hot with the pleasure of being with him again.

But it wouldn't do—because there was no way Matthew could be kept apart in this situation. There never would be.

'It was the coach that turned back into a pumpkin at midnight, not Cinderella!' she teased.

He shrugged unconcernedly, still smiling warmly down at her. 'I never was very good where fairy stories were concerned!'

Sapphie was, had known them all when she was a child. But she wasn't a child any longer, and she knew there could be no fairy-tale ending to this particular story. All she could hope for was to limit the damage. And the only way to do that, she knew, was to get out of here, as far away from Rik as possible.

'No, as I recall, Rik always preferred adventure stories,' his brother put in mockingly. 'Swashbuckling pirates and the like!'

It wasn't too difficult for Sapphie to imagine Rik as a little boy—after all, she had one just like him at home!—with his head buried in a book, totally absorbed in the adventures written there.

But that image—Matthew!—reminded her all too forcefully of why she had to leave. Now!

'Thanks, Nik,' Rik drawled ruefully before turning to Sapphie's mother. 'I'm Rik Prince, Mrs McCall.'

'Oh, dear,' Joan fluttered flusteredly. 'If your brother Zak walks in too, I shall just faint away!'

'Don't worry, Joan,' Juliet Prince was the one to answer laughingly. 'Zak is still away on his extended honeymoon.'

'Yes,' her husband joked. 'We may never see him or Tyler again!'

Juliet gave him a playful punch in the arm. 'You're only jealous because you're an old married man of three months!'

Nik gave her a wolfish grin that totally belied the 'old' part of that statement. 'I'll ask you to say that to me again later tonight, Mrs Prince!'

This family banter was all well and good, Sapphie acknowledged impatiently, but it was holding her back from getting her out of here. Despite several discreet attempts to release herself, Rik still had a tight hold of her hand! 'I really do have to leave—'

'No, you don't, Sapphie,' her mother was the one to answer her firmly. 'I think it would be much more appropriate if I was to leave and you stayed on here with your friends. You get out so little as it is—'

'Mother, I went to Paris for four days only last week,' Sapphie protested sharply. For one thing, none of the Prince family were her friends. For another, she knew by the tingling in her hand and up her arm that she really did have to get away from here. From Rik.

Just being near him again like this was doing strange things to her. Her cheeks felt permanently hot, her stomach was churning nervously. And as his hand held hers—his thumb was lightly caressing her palm now—she trembled all over.

She had to get away from him—and it was no longer just for Matthew's sake!

Rik watched Sapphie from beneath lowered lids, able to feel the turmoil inside her through her hand as it trembled slightly in his. He could also see the flush in her cheeks, and the vulnerability of her neck and throat, which were exposed by the way her hair was swept up in softly loose tendrils that lightly caressed her nape and temples.

His lips longed to caress her too!

She looked absolutely beautiful this evening: her gold-coloured silk dress shimmered against her curves, the high-necked knee-length style somehow managing to look as sexy as hell.

Although he had to admit, she could probably have worn a sack and he would still have found her sexy!

This last week of waiting to see her again had seemed more like a month to him, his patience stretched to its limits as he chafed against the delay. Nik had been the one to arrange their presence at tonight's party. Rik hadn't dared risk even a breath of his own attendance reaching Sapphie's ear; he knew her well enough by now to know that she would simply not have come if she'd known he was going to be here as well.

It had done absolutely nothing for his ego to admit that, and Nik had laughed himself almost to tears once Rik had explained the situation to him. Especially as it turned out that Nik knew a lot more about Diamond McCall than Rik ever had; apparently, her flirtations with her leading men were legendary amongst the movie set, and she'd even tried it on with Zak on one memorable occasion, but had failed miserably because of Zak's aversion to being involved with married women.

Rik still inwardly winced at Nik's reaction when he'd told his brother he had thought himself in love with Dee for the last five years. 'With Diamond McCall?' Nik had exclaimed. 'The woman is a walking, talking Venus fly-trap!'

'That really isn't helping Rik right now, darling,' Jinx had reproved concernedly.

Thank goodness for Jinx! She had been the one to come up with this evening's party as a way for him to see Sapphie again, even offering her own and Nik's presence as moral support. Knowing how much she hated these things, Rik had deeply appreciated—and quickly accepted—the offer, on the basis that Sapphie was less likely to just tell him to go away in front of his family!

'That was work, Sapphie,' her mother gently refuted her protest. 'I can easily take the car home that Jerome has put at our disposal this evening,' she offered. 'And you can come along later,' she urged evenly, smiling approvingly at Sapphie's hand, which was still held fast by Rik's.

Joan McCall wasn't part of the conspiracy to get Rik and Sapphie together, but at that moment she might just as well have been, Rik acknowledged admiringly.

Although he wasn't quite so pleased a second later when Sapphie pointedly removed her hand from his, obviously having also seen her mother's smiling approval.

Sapphie shook her head. 'You know I have an early start in the morning—'

'It isn't going to matter if you sleep in a little this once, Sapphie,' her mother insisted firmly. 'I want you to stay and have fun this evening. In fact, I insist upon it,' Joan McCall told her eldest daughter determinedly. 'Matthew isn't going to mind a bit once I've explained it to him.' She smiled encouragingly.

Matthew…!

There was the mention of that man again!

But if he was in Sapphie's life, then why wasn't he here with her tonight?

Damn it, the one time Rik had casually mentioned this Matthew to Jerome, the other man had dismissed him as not being a problem.

But Matthew certainly seemed like one at the moment if it meant Sapphie had to leave early because of him!

Sapphie, surprisingly, had gone very quiet after her mother's last remark, a fact Joan took advantage of as she made her hurried goodbyes before crossing the room to say goodnight to her youngest daughter.

Dee, predictably, was at the centre of an adoring crowd, a brilliant green butterfly shimmering above lesser mortals.

The vision left Rik cold. In fact, the more he learnt about Dee, the less he liked her. Why, oh, why hadn't he tried to find out more about her long ago? He could have saved himself years of heartache if he had. Forget Dee, he told himself impatiently, it was Sapphie who was important.

Sapphie was still incredibly quiet, he realised suddenly, and she seemed to have gone slightly pale now, too. Because her mother had mentioned Matthew? What sort of hold must the man have over her if she reacted in this way just at the mention of his name?

'If Matthew means so much to you, then why the hell isn't he here tonight—?' Rik broke off abruptly as Nik began to cough as if he were choking. A frowning glance from Rik in Nik's direction was rewarded by an impatient glare from his brother. Cool it, Nik's angry grey eyes warned exasperatedly.

Rik gave an inward wince at that unspoken warning, glad of the diversion created by Jinx, who set about acquiring a glass of champagne—totally unnecessary, as it happened—to help ease her husband's coughing fit. It gave Rik a chance to regain his jealous temper.

Nik was right; what was he trying to do, alienate Sapphie before the evening was out? He had already known about Matthew; his mission tonight was to encourage Sapphie to get to know him, to like being with him—not to annoy her to the point where she decided to leave!

'He wasn't invited,' Sapphie answered him stiffly now. 'And I really don't think—'

'We were just about to retire to one of the hotel bars for a quiet drink,' Jinx put in, Nik's coughing fit over as he sipped his fresh champagne with obvious enjoyment. 'Come on, Nik,' she linked her arm with her husband's, 'let's go and see if we can find a nice, quiet corner somewhere for the four of us to sit.'

Briefly leaving Rik alone with Sapphie. A tongue-tied Rik, as it happened. He had been thinking of this moment all week, and now that it was here he just didn't know what to say. How did you go about explaining to a woman that the dream woman you had been in love with for the last five years was nothing but a figment of your own imagination? That in the short time he had spent with Sapphie she had become so much more real to him? That he liked listening to her talk? That he just liked being with her, full stop?

That he was falling in love with her!

If he wasn't already in love with her...

He had debated long and hard this last week how he felt about her. He knew that he longed to see her again. That he loved the way she spoke so honestly to him. That he found her company stimulating. That just looking at her excited him in a way he wouldn't have believed possible.

But he also knew from previous conversations with her that it was going to take a lot more than words to convince Sapphie he was no longer in love with Dee—although the simple truth of the matter was, he never had been!

'You look wonderful,' he volunteered.

Sapphie gave him a startled look from those incredible amber-coloured eyes of hers, obviously not expecting the compliment after his earlier sharpness—he really would have to try to control his jealousy. Thank goodness Nik had managed to stop him this time before he completely alienated Sapphie all over again!

'Incredibly beautiful, in fact,' Rik added softly, rewarded by the blush that heightened her cheeks.

But, despite the blush, she remarked, 'Dee has always been the beautiful one of the family!' He probably deserved that, Rik accepted. Until they'd met again last week, and he'd come to realise how feisty and beautiful Sapphie was; apart from the odd wistful thought of that passionate night five years ago—and the odd guilty one too!—he hadn't really given Sapphie's feelings too much consideration. Sapphie had gone from his hotel suite the next morning before he'd even awoken; nothing, not even a tissue or used glass, had betrayed her presence there.

Not that Rik had told Nik and Jinx everything about what had happened when he'd slept with Sapphie; that would remain their secret, was no one else's business but their own!

'Shall we go and join the others?' Sapphie suggested stiffly. 'As it would appear that I'm not going to be allowed to leave until I've had at least one drink with you all!' she added impatiently before turning and striding off after Nik and Jinx.

At least, she tried to stride, but her dress, its silk material fitting snugly to her breasts, waist and thighs to just above her knees, made it impossible for her to do more than take small, elegant steps.

Rik caught up with her easily, taking a light hold of her elbow, matching his steps to hers before grinning down at her. 'I'm beginning to like your dress more and more!'

Sapphie shot him an exasperated glare for his trouble.

But she didn't come back with one of her sharp put-downs. And she didn't try to pull away from him again, either.

It was a start...

CHAPTER EIGHT

SAPPHIE was enjoying herself!

A glance at her wrist-watch told her it had been over an hour since she and Rik had joined Jinx and Nik in a quiet alcove in one of the hotel's public bars. An hour during which Nik had ordered another bottle of champagne to be served to the four of them and then he and his wife had gone out of their way, Sapphie was sure, to put her at her ease, regaling her and Rik with stories of the funnier side of their brief courtship and their marriage.

Sapphie was sure the champagne was helping her to relax too, but all the same, this meeting with Rik hadn't been as difficult as she had imagined it would be. There was no Dee around to sour things, for a start!

Although Sapphie still suspected that this whole encounter had been arranged by Rik, somehow. She wasn't sure how he had done it—or even why he should have bothered!—but she nevertheless felt the chance meeting with Nik and Jinx, and then Rik's appearance, had all been choreographed.

But she was still enjoying herself!

In fact, apart from that brief moment of panic earlier when her mother had mentioned Matthew, the evening had turned out to be nowhere near as traumatic as she had might have feared.

Apart from that brief moment of panic earlier when her mother had mentioned Matthew...!

At the time Sapphie had thought she was about to have a heart attack!

So far, mainly due to Dee's coy behaviour on the only other occasion Matthew's name had been mentioned, Rik seemed to have the impression that Matthew was the current man in her life, and certainly had no idea he was only four years old.

But he had come pretty close this evening to discovering the truth...

She shouldn't be enjoying herself, shouldn't relax her guard for a moment when she was around Rik!

'More champagne?' he offered attentively, holding the bottle over her half-empty wine glass.

'I don't think so, thank you,' she refused. 'I really should be going soon.'

Very soon. Before she relaxed too much and became incautious about what she said.

'Why?' Rik topped her champagne glass up anyway. 'I would have thought you worked from home.'

She did. But just because she might have had only a couple of hours' sleep didn't mean that her son—their son—wouldn't come bouncing into her bedroom at his usual six-thirty in the morning, expecting her to be as bright and happy as he was!

Admittedly she shared a house with her mother, and had done so since Matthew was born. But that was really only as moral support, Sapphie preferring, whenever possible, to take care of Matthew herself.

She absolutely adored him...!

'Actually, I think we're the ones who should be

going,' Nik Prince put in lightly. 'My wife issued me with a challenge earlier this evening—I would like to go home and collect on my success!' He smiled suggestively at his wife as he stood up before pulling Jinx to her feet beside him. 'It's been really nice meeting you again, Sapphie,' he told her pleasantly, his arm about his wife's shoulders now.

'Very nice,' Jinx echoed warmly, obviously quite happy at the thought of going home. 'Perhaps the two of you would like to come to dinner, say—Saturday evening?' she prompted brightly.

Sapphie blinked, taken totally aback by the invitation, let alone the phrase 'the two of you'!

Surely Nik and Jinx didn't think that she and Rik were really a couple? Admittedly, Rik had kissed her when he arrived, and held her hand for longer than was really necessary, but even so...

No, she decided as she watched the two brothers exchange a knowing look. This was another ploy on Rik's part, she was sure; the invitation had nothing to do with what had happened this evening and everything to do with preplanning on the part of the Prince family.

Her mouth set mutinously, she shot Rik a resentful glare as she stood up. 'No, I don't think—'

'How about I call you tomorrow, Jinx, and let you know?' Rik cut in smoothly as he stood up too. 'Sapphie probably has to check her diary or something.' His arm moved lightly about Sapphie's waist.

Her diary, as Sapphie well knew, was completely empty of future engagements; she just didn't like being manoeuvred in this way!

'No—'

'Yes, please do call me, Rik.' Jinx moved forward to kiss him warmly on the cheek before moving to do the same to Sapphie. 'I really have enjoyed meeting you this evening, Sapphie, and we'd love for you to come to dinner on Saturday.' Her clear eyes looked steadily into Sapphie's.

There was no doubting the other woman's sincerity, just as there was no doubt in Sapphie's mind that she had enjoyed meeting Jinx and her husband. Rik was the problem here…just being anywhere near him.

Because she was so totally aware of him, found her defences weakening the longer she was with him. She'd already fallen into that trap once. Once was an accident, twice was just pure stupidity!

'I'll try,' she murmured noncommittally, very aware of the warmth of Rik's arm about her waist.

'Good.' Jinx squeezed her arm.

Sapphie managed to keep the smile on her lips for as long as it took Jinx and Nik to leave. At which time she turned furiously on Rik. 'You arranged all this!' she accused, eyes blazing. 'Your brother and his wife! The two of us meeting! The invitation to dinner on Saturday evening!' She glared at Rik, breathing hard in her agitation.

Rik continued to look at her for several seconds, and then he nodded. 'Yes.'

Her eyes widened. 'What did you say?'

'I said yes,' he repeated patiently. 'It was all pre-arranged. The meeting with Nik and Jinx to break the ice. My own arrival a few minutes later. The dinner invitation just now.' He sighed. 'Why don't we sit down and—?'

'I don't want to sit down,' she flung back, stung by his easy acquiescence to her accusations; she had at least expected him to attempt to deny them! But then, when did Rik ever do what she expected him to do…? 'I want to know the reason you did all that.'

'I wanted to see you again. You made it very clear, the last time we met, that you didn't want to see me—'

'For obvious reasons!' Sapphie reminded him. 'Just because Dee stole the man I loved does not mean I need you to fill the gap!'

Rik gave a smile. 'Dee doesn't love me. She never did.' Sapphie knew that, knew that Dee loved Jerome as much as she was capable of loving anyone other than herself. But that didn't necessarily change the way Rik had always felt about Dee…

'That may be so,' Sapphie retorted. 'But *you* still love *her*—and she knows it.'

He quirked dark brows quizzically. 'I'm not answerable for what Dee does or doesn't know—or thinks she knows,' he replied softly.

She looked at him searchingly. What did he mean? Was he saying that…?

She gave an impatient shake of her head. 'I don't have the time for this.' She bent to pick up her evening bag. 'It's been—different,' she said. 'But now I have to go.' Because she was past anger, and now felt as if she was about to cry…!

'I'll walk outside with you and make sure you—'

'Rik—don't!' she choked, her head down, her vision now blurred by unshed tears. 'I—I like my life exactly the way that it is. I was happy! I don't want—don't want—'

'Sapphie, are you crying?' Rik groaned, lightly grasping her arm to turn her to face him. 'You are! Damn it—I never meant to make you cry!'

'Then what did you mean to do?' she demanded emotionally. 'Why go to all this trouble—?'

'It was no trouble, Sapphie,' he assured her huskily. 'And I had asked to see you again,' he reminded her, 'but you said no.'

'For very good reason!' She nodded. 'I didn't want to see you again.' What she really wanted with this man, and what she could actually have, were two distinctly different things! 'No matter what impression you may have to the contrary, Rik, I do not indulge in affairs!' No matter what she might have told him—out of pure self-defence!—there had been no other lovers in her life but Rik. She hadn't wanted any…

But she did still want Rik; her traitorous body told her so every time she was near him. As she wanted him now…!

'I really do have to go, Rik.' Before she made a complete idiot of herself!

And they had already attracted enough attention for one evening, she realised as she saw the curious looks being sent their way by the other people in the bar.

Too much attention for Sapphie's comfort. She turned on her heel to walk quickly out of the room, across the reception area and outside into the refreshing night air, breathing it in deeply as she fought the compulsion to be sick.

'Sapphie…?'

She had no defences left, no strength to fight Rik, who had followed her outside. He took her into his arms, his brilliant blue gaze holding hers briefly before he lowered his head and his mouth claimed hers.

Oh…!

Her need for this man was just too much for her to resist, her lips parting beneath his even as her arms moved up over his shoulders and her fingers became entwined in the silky dark hair at his nape.

With a low groan in his throat Rik deepened the kiss, his arms tightening about her waist as he moulded her slender curves to the harder planes of his body.

Nothing had changed, Sapphie acknowledged achingly; she loved and wanted this man. Only this man. She realised now that she always would.

'Sapphie!' Rik husked now, his lips moving to the warm sensitivity of her throat. 'Sapphie!' he murmured achingly, his hands moving restlessly along the length of her spine, his tongue seeking the hollows at the base of her neck, his breath warm against her already overheated skin. 'I want you, Sapphie.' His voice was intent as he raised his head to look at her. 'Sapphie, please—'

'No!' she managed to gasp weakly, desperately seeking the strength to pull away from him. And failing.

'You want me too, Sapphie,' he insisted as her body continued to betray her. 'Stop fighting me, darling—'

'I am not your darling,' she burst out, at the same

time pushing ineffectually at his shoulders. 'Rik, let me go! You have to let me go!' she pleaded as he made no effort to do so. 'Don't you understand it yet that there's simply no room in my life for you?' This last was intended to hurt.

And she had succeeded if the darkening of his expression was anything to go by. His arms moved up to grasp her arms. 'I didn't imagine your response just now,' he grated harshly. 'Or in Paris. Or in London when we said goodbye—'

'Exactly—we said goodbye, Rik,' she reminded him. 'As for my responding to you...' She made her voice as hard as she could. 'So you're a more than competent lover—what does that prove?' She looked at him with challenge, while all the while her heart was breaking inside at the deliberate gulf she was putting between the two of them.

Rik frowned ominously even as he returned her stare. 'What does it prove?' he bit out. 'Well, for one thing, it proves you aren't in love with anyone called Matthew!'

Sapphie felt herself sway as her knees went weak, all of the colour draining from her face as she looked at him with wide, amber-bruised eyes.

Rik watched the change that came over her with ever-increasing dismay. And puzzlement. Why had the mere mention of the other man's name have such a physical as well as emotional effect on her? What hold did this man have on Sapphie to make her react in this way?

She drew in a deep breath, seeming to gather herself up, glaring at him with fiercely intense eyes now, the colour returned to her cheeks as her anger grew. 'You're wrong; I love Matthew with every fibre of my being!'

The words were like nails in Rik's flesh, his hands falling helplessly to his sides as he stared at her disbelievingly.

'He's the last thing I think of before I go to sleep at night,' Sapphie continued emotionally. 'The first person I think of when I wake in the morning. And if, for any reason, I should ever feel sad or dispirited,' her voice grew stronger, 'then I just have to think of Matthew's smile, a smile that's only for me, and then nothing seems quite as bad as I thought it was.' Amber eyes looked steadily into his now. 'Isn't that love?'

Rik blinked dazedly. It certainly sounded like it to him; was the way he had been thinking of Sapphie since they'd met up again in Paris.

Too late.

Damn it, he was always too late!

He didn't know what to say in answer to her challenge. Telling her how he felt now seemed a waste of time. His as well as hers.

He'd had his chance with this woman five years ago, and well and truly blown it; it was too much to hope, too much to ask, that a woman as beautiful as Sapphie would still be free after all this time. Sheer bloody arrogance on his part, in fact!

He gave a humourless smile. 'It certainly sounds a lot like it!' he allowed heavily.

'Good,' she dismissed briskly. 'At least we're

agreed on something! Now, if you don't mind, I'm going home.' She signalled the first cab waiting in the line outside the hotel. 'Why don't you go back inside and enjoy the party?' she suggested offhandedly as she got in the back of the cab and closed the door firmly behind her.

Rik stood on the pavement and watched the cab as it pulled away, continuing to watch it until it was swallowed up in the late-night traffic.

He couldn't move. Didn't want to move, felt as if once he went back into the hotel he would be shutting a door on Sapphie.

Instead he turned on his heel, hands in his pockets, and began to walk towards the River Thames.

He had always found something soothing about moving water; his mother had claimed it was because she swam in the ocean all the time when she was pregnant with him. Maybe she was right, because minutes later, staring down into the moon-reflected water, he felt a certain calm moving over and into him.

Sapphie said she loved this Matthew, and her sincerity had rung true. But at the same time Rik knew that she wouldn't—couldn't—have responded to him in that way if she really was *in love* with this other man.

But was that of any help to him in the face of Sapphie's obstinate claim that she loved Matthew?

He had absolutely no idea, he realised, of what he was going to do next.

Which was why he was in no mood, having walked back to the hotel—he had booked a suite there for the night—to get into conversation with Jerome Powers, of all people!

Sapphie had once loved this man, had been about to marry him, would have married him if Dee hadn't come along and taken him for herself. Ridiculously, Rik found himself jealous even of that past love.

'Hi, Rik,' the other man greeted him jovially, seemingly impervious to Rik's scowl. 'I just came out to check on where the four of you had got to.'

'The others have all gone home, and I'm just on my way upstairs to bed,' Rik answered Jerome flatly, just wanting to get away, to be on his own, to lick his wounds in private.

Jerome grinned unconcernedly. 'Feeling lucky, were you?' he said smugly. 'That sort of thing isn't going to work with Sapphie, I'm afraid. Once bitten, twice shy and all that.' Considering Jerome was the 'once bitten' part of that statement, Rik found his attitude less than charming.

He shook his head, his hands clenched at his sides as he resisted the impulse to actually hit the older man. 'I would really rather not talk about Sapphie, if you don't mind!' He had no objection to talking with Sapphie, but he certainly wasn't going to talk about her. Especially with Jerome Powers! 'And shouldn't you be getting back to your wife rather than out here looking for Sapphie?' he prompted pointedly.

Jerome's smile widened proudly. 'Doesn't Dee-Dee look absolutely stunning this evening?' now left him absolutely cold—it was auburn fire that he wanted.

'You're right, I should get back,' Jerome agreed.

'But I wouldn't give up on Sapphie if I were you; I can see that she likes you really.'

Liking him was one thing—and he wasn't convinced that she did like him!—but Rik wanted more than that. So much more! And he wasn't even sure when—or even if—he was ever going to see her again.

Simply going and knocking on her door hadn't seemed like an option after the way they had parted at the railway station last week, which was why he had organised such a convoluted meeting this evening. But, from Sapphie's reaction, he knew for sure that something like that wasn't going to work a second time.

After the things Sapphie had said to him tonight he wasn't certain there was any point, either.

Damn it, he had never bothered with a hotel-room bar before in his life, but right now it seemed very tempting! Drunk had to be better than this aching pain.

Somewhere after the fourth glass of whisky—or could it have been the third gin?—he must have drifted off to sleep, because when the loud ringing of the telephone woke him some time the next morning he found himself slumped in an armchair, still wearing his dinner suit.

He sat up quickly, only to collapse back down again as his head threatened to explode. And still the telephone continued to ring in that mind-shattering way.

He made a grab for the receiver, dropping it with a clatter the first time, then finally managing to bring the receiver up to his ear. 'Whoever you are, please go away,' he groaned, feeling as if he had scrambled eggs for brains and cotton wool in his mouth; this getting drunk was way overrated, he decided.

A hearty laugh sounding down the telephone line made him wince. 'You don't sound too good, little brother,' Nik drawled with obvious amusement.

'I'll let you know about that later—at the moment I'm just trying to keep my head on my shoulders!'

Nik gave another chuckle. 'I gather things didn't go well after we left last night?'

Rik shut his eyes at that understatement. 'You could say that.'

'I just did,' his eldest brother returned. 'But the reason I rang is that I've just had a very interesting business meeting with Jerome—did you know he and Dee are flying back to the States this afternoon?'

Didn't know. Didn't care. And he wasn't in any sort of mood to discuss business.

'What the hell is the time?' Rik opened his eyes and tried to focus on his wrist-watch, finally managing to make out that it was eleven-thirty; not surprising really when he must have gone to sleep—passed out?—at around four-thirty. At least he'd had the foresight to put the 'Do Not Disturb' notice on his door! 'Nik, I'm really not awake yet, so can I call you back after I've showered and dressed?'

'No problem,' Nik accepted. 'Although I really only called to tell you that, according to Jerome, the reason Sapphie is so wary of becoming involved with anyone is that she has a young child. The father left her literally holding the baby, apparently, and...'

Rik was no longer listening, felt completely numb. And this time it had nothing to do with the drink he had consumed into the wee small hours.

A child. Sapphie had a child. What the hell—?

'A little boy.' Nik's words penetrated again. 'By the name of Matthew.'

It wasn't another man at all that she talked of with such love, but her own child...

Rik knew what he had to do!

CHAPTER NINE

'Do you ever intend to tell him that he has a son?'

Sapphie's face paled as she looked across the kitchen table at her mother. The two of them were enjoying a late-morning cup of coffee together, while Matthew happily sat on the floor at their feet, totally engrossed in a box of special building bricks he'd been given on his fourth birthday a couple of months ago.

Sapphie hadn't slept well. In fact, when Matthew had come into her bedroom this morning at his usual time of six-thirty she wasn't sure she had been to sleep at all, images of the evening running again and again through her head.

'Sorry?' She looked dazedly at her mother, not quite sure she had heard her correctly.

'I thought, at first, when you introduced me to Nik Prince and his lovely young wife that he was Matthew's father, the likeness was so noticeable. Which, considering his recent marriage, would have been something of a disaster,' her mother opined. 'But once Rik Prince arrived, I realised how mistaken I had been. So, I repeat, Sapphie,' she pressed, her frown troubled now, 'are you going to tell him about Matthew?'

Sapphie swallowed hard, having had no idea until this moment that her mother had noticed Rik's resemblance to Matthew; Joan had already been in bed, fast asleep, when Sapphie got in last night. She'd checked on Matthew before she went to bed herself and had found that he was fast asleep too, his small, loose-limbed body sprawled sideways across the bed, dark curls framing his cherubic features.

His resemblance to Rik had made her heart ache.

But she was stunned now by her mother's quietly posed question; it simply hadn't occurred to her that once her mother had seen Rik she would realise he was Matthew's father!

She swallowed hard. 'I hadn't intended to, no,' she said gruffly, knowing there was absolutely no point in trying to deny something that was so glaringly obvious to someone who knew Matthew so well and had now met Rik.

Her mother sipped her own coffee before answering. 'Why not?'

'You can ask me that?' Sapphie gasped, shooting a concerned glance at Matthew as he looked up curiously, her reassuring smile enough for him to go back to his building bricks. 'Can you imagine what that would do to Matthew's life?' she asked her mother softly. 'An English mother and an American father; he would become a human ping-pong ball, bouncing across the Atlantic!' She looked worried at the thought.

'It may not come to that—'

'Of course it will come to that!' Sapphie insisted agitatedly.

'But Rik Prince so obviously likes you—'

'Well, of course he likes me—he wants to go to

bed with me!' Again, she could have added, but didn't.

Her mother looked troubled. 'I've never pressed you for the identity of Matthew's father; I've tried to respect the fact that you didn't want to talk about him and told myself that you knew best. But now that I've actually met him…!' Joan shook her head. 'It doesn't seem right somehow. He seems like a nice man, a responsible man—'

'He's both those things,' Sapphie allowed; after all, she was in love with him—she could hardly make him out to be some sort of monster!

'I thought so,' her mother rejoined. 'Couldn't the two of you try to make a go of it? Perhaps even get married—'

'And live happily ever after?' Sapphie cut in fiercely. 'This is the real world, Mother, not a fairy story!'

'I do know that, Sapphie,' Joan answered quietly. 'I'm fifty-two years old, and I've been widowed twice; of course I know that.'

Of course she did, Sapphie acknowledged guiltily; her mother never talked of loneliness, always seemed happy, kept herself occupied with her bridge and gardening clubs. But that didn't mean she hadn't sometimes been lonely and unhappy during the last twelve years.

Although Matthew, Sapphie knew, had helped to fill some of that gaping hole in her mother's life; Joan would be someone else who would be hugely affected if Rik was told of his son, though she doubted her mother had thought that far ahead…

'I know you do.' She reached over and squeezed her mother's hand understandingly. 'It's just—' She broke off as the ringing of the doorbell interrupted them.

'That will be the postman.' Her mother stood up. 'I'm expecting a parcel.'

Sapphie watched her mother leave before glancing down at Matthew, maternal pride swelling in her chest; he really was a beautiful boy, and so happily secure in the world they had made for him here. She would not allow him to become a tug-of-love child, or his security to be ripped asunder. No matter how much she might love his father...

'We've a visitor,' her mother said woodenly as she came back into the kitchen, her face slightly pale. 'You've got a visitor, Sapphie,' she added softly. 'I've put him in the sitting-room.'

Sapphie tensed. 'Him?' she repeated warily.

But she knew who her visitor was without her mother needing to answer; only one person could have had this effect upon her mother: Rik.

She put her cup down slowly and stood up. 'Will you keep Matthew in here with you?' Her eyes pleaded with her mother to co-operate, to continue to respect her decision where Matthew's father was concerned.

'I'll try.' Joan nodded ruefully. 'But you know what he's like about visitors.'

Yes, she did know. Her young son was gregarious, not at all shy about meeting new people; in fact, he loved them. 'Just try,' she encouraged huskily, her hands feeling icy cold, and yet at the same time her palms were damp.

What was Rik doing here?

More to the point, how could she get rid of him before he discovered the truth about Matthew?

She was sure that last night he had believed Matthew to be another man, that without actually resorting to lies she had compounded that impression by talking about how much she loved him.

And yet, less than twelve hours later, Rik was here, in her home. In Matthew's home…!

She ran her damp palms down her denim-clad thighs, then drew in a deep, controlling breath before entering the sitting-room.

If she looked bad after a relatively sleepless night, then Rik looked much worse, his face very pale, lines of strain beside his nose and mouth, though sunglasses prevented her from reading the expression in his eyes.

It was this that she grasped on to. 'I thought it was raining outside?' she said derisively.

'It is,' he agreed, reaching up to remove the sunglasses, revealing the dark circles beneath his eyes, the light actually making him wince. 'Never mix champagne, whisky and gin,' he drawled. 'It's a lethal combination!' He placed the sunglasses back on his nose.

At any other time Sapphie might have found his discomfort amusing. But not today. Not with Matthew only feet away.

She looked at him coldly. 'What are you doing here, Rik? What do you want?'

'A gallon of black coffee might help,' he suggested. 'Although I wouldn't put a bet on it!'

'Sounds like you had a good time after I left last night,' she said drily, not sitting down, and not asking him to either—even though he did look as if he might fall down at any moment. But she was too restless to sit down, and he wouldn't be staying long enough to make himself comfortable!

'A bad one,' he corrected her. 'And on that basis, I suppose things can only get better. In fact, as far as I'm concerned, they already have. Sapphie, why didn't you just tell me that Matthew is your son?'

Rik was wrong—this situation had just become a hundred times worse!

Rik watched as Sapphie moved to sit down abruptly in one of the armchairs, her face rigid with shock as she stared up at him with haunted amber-coloured eyes. 'Who told you?' she choked, her gaze sharpening suddenly. 'Was it Dee? Because if it was—'

'It wasn't Dee,' Rik assured her soothingly, noticing the look of relief that flooded her eyes. 'Look, Sapphie,' he moved to go down on his haunches beside her chair, taking one of her cold hands into the warmth of his, 'doesn't my being here tell you that it makes no difference to me? That you could have six children and I would still want you?' And he knew that it was true, that he wanted Sapphie, no matter what baggage she brought along with her.

As he'd stood beneath a stinging hot shower earlier for ten minutes, trying to see the situation from her point of view, he'd realised that it was love for her child that had made her behave so defensively, that had made her so determined to push other relationships from her life. To push him from her life. It was up to him to change all that.

Sapphie swallowed hard, eyeing him warily now. 'You would?'

'Yes—I would,' he came back firmly.

Nik had tried, in his usual big-brother fashion, to give him advice on the telephone earlier that morning, urging him to remember that a single mother came as part of a package, and that he would have to bond with the child as much as the mother, and to remember that all the time he was doing this bonding with the mother and the son the child's real father was out there somewhere doing his damnedest to ensure that he didn't succeed!

At which point Rik had come back with, 'And if it had been Jinx in the same circumstances?'

'I would still have fallen in love and married her,' Nik had answered without hesitation.

Exactly. That was exactly how Rik felt about Sapphie. OK, so she was a little prickly because of her circumstances; he would just have to overcome her distrust. And how hard could it be to bond with a small child who wasn't yet mature enough to have formed many likes and dislikes?

Although he wasn't quite so sure about that when, the very next moment, a small voice somewhere else in the house began to cry out, 'I want my mummy! I want my mummy!'

Sapphie tensed at the very first cry, snatching her hand out of his to stand up. 'You have to leave—'

The door was flung open suddenly, silencing her, a small tornado hurtling into the room and into her waiting arms. 'Mummy!' the little boy cried determinedly. 'I wanted to show you my tower, but Nana said you were busy.' He turned to give his grandmother an accusing look as she stood behind him in the open doorway.

Having expected a baby, or, at the most, a small toddler, Rik was rather surprised that Matthew was quite this big—and this vocal!

Sapphie bent down and swept the little boy up into her arms. Matthew's height and sturdiness showed him to be a little boy of about four—or five?—years old, with glossy dark curls framing his still-babyish features. As he turned, Rik found himself the curious focus of the child's deep blue eyes.

'It's a man,' he told his mother brightly.

No, not just a man, Rik realised as he continued to study the little boy. All of the colour drained from his face as he looked at a replica of himself at four years old: the same tall-for-his-age body, those dark, glossy curls, the same blue eyes. No, not just a man—Matthew's father!

This little boy—four years and two months old if Rik's memory was correct—was his son!

He couldn't breathe. Couldn't speak. Damn—he wasn't sure he was going to be able to stand on his own two feet for very much longer!

Sapphie's child was his child. His son. Matthew was his son!

'I'm so sorry.' Joan was the one to break the silence as she spoke pleadingly to her daughter. 'I tried to stop him, but…' She gave a helpless movement of her hands.

Joan McCall, a woman he had grown to like the previous evening, knew that Matthew was his son, too! Why else would she be quite this upset, so apologetic?

'It's OK,' Sapphie assured her mother huskily. 'Maybe—maybe it's for the best.' She turned to look enquiringly at Rik, her arms tightening about Matthew as she saw the completely stunned expression on Rik's face.

He still couldn't speak, could only continue to stare at Matthew. He was such a beautiful child, so much a little boy already, so—so his!

And he had already missed four years of his son's life…

Because of Sapphie. Because she had chosen five years ago not to tell him she was expecting his child.

Why had she done that? What right did she have to have made that decision alone, to have kept Matthew a secret from him for all these years?

Anger started to replace the numbness, blinding, white-hot anger. 'God damn you, Sapphie!' he rasped harshly.

'The man swore, Mummy,' Matthew gasped, blue eyes wide. 'He's a bad man.'

'No, not a bad man, darling,' Sapphie assured him huskily. 'Just a very angry one, I think.' She raised questioning brows in Rik's direction.

'Anger doesn't even begin to describe how I feel at this moment,' he ground out fiercely.

What he wanted, more than anything, was to reach

out and take his son in his arms, to crush him to him, to know the wonder of holding his own flesh and blood!

But he couldn't do that; he was nothing but a stranger to Matthew, a 'bad man' who swore at his mother…!

Sapphie drew in a sharp breath at the violence she must have seen in his expression. 'This isn't the time or the place for this, Rik,' she began to reason.

'You're right—it isn't,' he bit out forcefully, exerting every ounce of will-power he possessed to keep a lid on the anger that threatened to explode from him. For Matthew's sake. For his son's sake!

He still couldn't quite take all of this in, and yet he knew it was the truth, the evidence—Matthew's likeness to him so blazingly, obviously, right here before him. But if he needed any other confirmation then Sapphie's look of despair, and Joan's concern as she looked at both her daughter and her grandson were enough to convince him.

Over the last week he had grown to heartily dislike a man by the name of Matthew, to resent the part he played in Sapphie's life. But the overwhelming love he felt now as he looked at his son was almost enough to bring him to his knees!

He shook his head weakly. 'You're right, Sapphie; the time and place for this is a court of law!'

'No—' Joan cried.

'Rik, please!' Sapphie groaned emotionally.

'Please!' he repeated furiously. 'Please?' he said again less forcefully as Matthew scowled at him fiercely—for shouting at his beloved.

Sapphie was right, Rik acknowledged hardly, they couldn't talk about this in front of Matthew. That would only serve to alienate the little boy more. And that was the last thing he wanted.

What he wanted at this moment—Matthew!—he couldn't have. Which left him only one course of action.

'You can expect to hear from my lawyers,' he stated harshly.

'Rik, no!' Sapphie gasped again.

'Rik, yes!' he said coldly, taking one last knee-weakening look at Matthew before striding to the door, giving Joan McCall a look of reproach as he passed her in the doorway.

But he would be back.

And soon!

CHAPTER TEN

'WELL, that could have gone better, couldn't it?' Sapphie murmured weakly even as she sat down in one of the armchairs, Matthew on her knee. Her legs were shaking so badly that if she didn't sit down, she knew she would fall down.

Matthew climbed off her knee. 'He was a naughty man, Mummy. He swored.' But his last comment was only made distractedly as he spotted his box of toys behind the sofa and made a beeline for his favourite fire-engine.

'I think he had good reason to swear,' Sapphie's mother sighed, having stepped aside as Rik left or risked being trampled underfoot. 'Sapphie, can you imagine how that poor man feels—?'

'Yes! Yes, I can,' she acknowledged shakily.

And she could; she knew how she would feel if Matthew were suddenly produced as her child. Wondrous at the beautiful miracle of him, but angry too at the person who had deprived her of the first four years of his life. In this case, that was her…

'What do I do about this?' She looked at her mother desperately. 'You heard him—he's going to make it a legal battle!' Her voice rose in panic.

Because she knew it was a battle she was likely to lose. Rik hadn't abandoned his child, he simply hadn't known of his existence. Plus he was a rich and powerful man, and his reputation was unimpeachable.

'You can't let it get to that, Sapphie,' her mother echoed her own thoughts. 'Admittedly, a court usually comes down in favour of the mother, and I'm sure that they would this time too, but Rik is entitled to have access to his son. He's a wealthy man, and his lawyers are bound to be the best there are—'

'You aren't making me feel better, Mother!' Sapphie replied, her eyes welling with tears.

'I don't mean to upset you, Sapphie,' her mother sympathised, moving to squeeze her arm reassuringly. 'Really, I don't,' she urged. 'But I was watching his face the whole time, saw the way he looked at Matthew! Sapphie, it was that same look of pride and fierce protectiveness you see on every new parent's face!'

She knew that, had seen it too; Rik already loved Matthew with a fierce paternal love.

Taking that into account, and the way he felt about her at the moment—so angry he had looked capable of strangling her!—then she knew he wasn't likely to settle for anything less than complete access to Matthew. She doubted very much that Rik would succeed in taking Matthew away from her—her own reputation was as unimpeachable as his—but the ensuing battle would probably ensure that Sapphie and Rik ended up hating each other for the rest of their lives!

'I have to go and talk to him,' she decided determinedly as she stood up.

Her mother nodded. 'I think that's very wise—'

'But I can't!' Sapphie groaned frustratedly.

'You have to—'

'No, Mother, I meant that I can't go and talk to Rik because I have no idea where he's staying!' Sapphie explained desperately. 'It's just never come up in conversation,' she defended as her mother looked at her disbelievingly.

'But surely—someone must know where he can be reached,' her mother reasoned impatiently.

Dee, Sapphie thought instantly. Much as she hated to acknowledge it, Dee was sure to know where Rik was staying while he was in London.

But did she really want to go to Dee cap in hand and ask her about the whereabouts of her ex-lover?

Did she have any other choice?

'You're lucky to have caught us, Sapphie,' Jerome informed her lightly as he answered her call to his mobile.

Sapphie had totally forgotten that Dee and Jerome were leaving later today to go back to the States. Not surprising really, given the circumstances! She only hoped that luck would continue for the rest of what promised to be a traumatic day...

'Rik?' Jerome echoed after Sapphie had told him the reason she was calling—if not the reason she so desperately needed to find Rik! 'Well, he was staying here at this hotel last night—'

'That's all I needed to know!' Sapphie breathed with relief. 'And to wish the two of you a safe journey home, of course,' she added quickly as she realised how that must have sounded.

'Of course,' Jerome echoed drily. 'And you didn't let me finish just now; I said Rik was staying at the hotel last night, but it's my understanding that he booked out early this morning.'

Sapphie felt herself deflate again. Obviously Rik had come here after he'd signed out of the hotel, but where had he gone now? She had no idea. Had no idea of anything concerning Rik's private life! But his life had overspilled into her own now, and in the circumstances, she had to find him!

'You really do need to reach him, huh?' Jerome probed gently at her continued silence. 'Did the two of you have a fight or something last night? Only he seemed a little down, after you left.'

'A little down' didn't at all describe the way Rik was when he stormed out of her home a short time ago! Murderous was probably more apt!

'I just need to talk to him about something,' she answered evasively. 'But if you don't have any idea where he is, then—'

'I don't—but Nik Prince is sure to know. And I do have a number where he can be reached,' Jerome assured her with satisfaction.

Nik Prince? The man had been pleasant enough last night, but once Rik had told him of the way she had kept his son's existence a secret from him for the last five years, she very much doubted that would continue! Even on such a brief acquaintance, she knew that Nik Prince would be a formidable enemy.

More formidable than Rik was at this moment?

The answer to that was a definite no!

'OK,' she sighed. 'If you wouldn't mind giving me that number…?'

'Just a second,' Jerome dismissed. 'Dee, honey,

would you just come and talk to Sapphie while I get my Filofax from my briefcase?'

'Hi, Sapph, what's going on?' her sister demanded bluntly.

'I—er—I have one of the buttons from Rik's suit in my bag,' she invented lamely! 'It dropped off last night and I just wanted to return it to him.' Lame. Very lame!

'Aren't you being a little obvious, Sapphie?' Dee drawled, not fooled for a moment. 'Haven't you learnt yet that if you have to run after a man, then he isn't worth bothering with?'

Was that the reason that, even after five years of marriage, Jerome was the one who still did all the running? Probably, Sapphie acknowledged ruefully. But if it worked for them...

But, unfortunately, their relationship bore absolutely no resemblance to her own present situation!

'I'll explain some other time, Dee,' she moved on briskly, knowing that soon, if Rik was to continue with his intention of involving lawyers, everyone was going to know that Sapphie Benedict was the mother of his son... 'Right now I just need to contact Rik.'

'Well, don't say I didn't try to warn you,' Dee replied before putting her husband back on the line, with an audible caution to him not to be too long.

Sapphie forgot all about Dee's warning as soon as the call was ended, staring for a good five minutes at the piece of paper where she had written down Nik Prince's telephone number.

What was she going to say to Rik's brother? Would

he, like Dee, think that the button was just a ruse, and that she was chasing his youngest brother?

What did it really matter what Nik Prince thought about her now when pretty soon he, and the rest of the Prince family were going to be told they had one more to add to their number!

For all she knew, Nik Prince might already have been told about his nephew!

'Will you just back up a few sentences?' Nik frowned darkly, standing across the room from where Rik paced up and down in front of the unlit fireplace.

Rik came to a halt. Sapphie hadn't told him he had a son. *A son.* Every time he thought of Matthew he felt as if he was going to fall down on his knees at the wonder of him.

He had arrived at Nik and Jinx's a short time ago and, so far, he knew, he hadn't made a great deal of sense. Because his brain wasn't functioning properly, and his heart felt as if it was about to burst!

'Does this have anything to do with what I told you earlier about Matthew?' Nik guessed shrewdly.

Did it have anything to do with Matthew…?

It had everything to do with Matthew. And he couldn't think about Matthew without thinking about Sapphie, too.

Sapphie…!

Every time he thought about her he felt driven to his knees, too. His emotions were so confused; on the one hand he was so angry with her for keeping her pregnancy, and consequently Matthew's birth, a secret, but on the other he was full of admiration for the way she had dealt so capably with both those things. She hadn't just dealt with them, with Matthew, she had excelled; Matthew was a beautiful and intelligent child.

He'd had Rik figured as a 'bad man' within minutes of meeting him!

And no wonder Sapphie had looked as if she hated the sight of him when they'd met again in Paris. It also explained her determination that Dee and Jerome shouldn't know they had ever met before. Met—they had created Matthew!

'Rik, what—' Nik broke off to glare impatiently at the telephone as it began to ring.

'I should answer that if I were you,' Rik advised drily, knowing that Jinx had gone out with her father this morning. 'I know I'm not making a lot of sense at the moment!'

Because this was just so big. So onerous. It was going to blow the family's minds once they knew about Matthew. Rik was the loner, the private, reserved one, the one who was always there to advise the rest of the family. But now he was the one who was falling apart!

He desperately wanted to see Matthew again. Just wanted to look at him, to breathe him in. All he had wanted to do earlier was pick him up and walk out of there with him. And what would that have achieved? A broken-hearted mother and son—and possibly a father in a police cell.

For once in his life he didn't know what to do next. In his anger this morning, he had threatened Sapphie with lawyers; he wasn't stupid enough—stunned

enough!—to believe he would ever win a custody
fight for a little boy who didn't even know him. But
he would have a right to see him, despite the fact that
his mother so obviously didn't want to share him.

He was back to Sapphie again…

He still didn't know how he felt about her now!
Part of him could have strangled her for not coming
to him five years ago, for not telling him about the
baby she was expecting. His baby. But another part
of him wanted to kiss her for giving him such a beautiful son. He wasn't—

His attention focused on Nik as he realised that,
although his brother was talking into the receiver, he
was actually looking at him while he did so.

'There's no need for that; he's right here.' Nik
spoke tersely. 'No, I don't think he's going anywhere
any time soon, so why don't you just come over here?
No, it's no trouble,' he responded to the next question
before reciting the address of the house he and Jinx
shared with Jinx's father. 'See you soon, then,
Sapphie,' he said politely before ending the call.

Sapphie. That had been Sapphie on the telephone?
And she was coming here?

Why? To threaten him as he had threatened her?
Or to cajole him into seeing that he had no part to
play in Matthew's life? Neither of those options ap-
pealed to him!

Although he had to admire Sapphie for trying…

'Sapphie mentioned something about meeting on
neutral ground,' Nik told him darkly. 'Exactly what
have you been doing to that lovely lady, little

brother?' He glowered at Rik from beneath lowered brows.

Rik hadn't actually done anything yet. Neither would he, having already come to his senses enough to know he was on a hiding to nothing if he took Sapphie to court to gain custody. But Sapphie didn't know that!

'I can't talk about it yet, Nik.' He shook his head.

'Fine,' his brother replied. 'I'll go make us both some coffee.'

The coffee, and the waiting, didn't improve Rik's mood; Nik was treating him as if he had been drinking this morning too. And maybe to his brother it did seem that way; he certainly wasn't making a lot of sense!

But when the doorbell finally rang to announce Sapphie's arrival, he knew that he couldn't just leave his brother in the dark like this, that he owed Nik an explanation, at least.

He drew in a deep breath, standing up to pace the room again. 'Nik, in a minute or two you're going to hear something…' He stopped, not sure how to continue, but knowing time was running out, that the housekeeper must have answered the door by now, that Sapphie was on her way in here. 'Nik, Matthew is my son, OK?' he burst out, having decided there really was no easy way to say it.

The dark thundercloud that suddenly gathered in Nik's face was probably very reminiscent of Rik's own reaction earlier this morning!

'No!' Nik exclaimed. 'It is not OK.' He looked at Rik as if seeing him for the first time.

No, Rik accepted leadenly, it really wasn't OK.

And from the bleak look on Sapphie's white face as she was shown into the sitting-room, it wasn't OK with her, either; the look she gave him from beneath her long, dark lashes was wary to say the least.

Rik's first instinct was to wrap her in his arms and keep her safe, to assure her that he would never let anyone hurt her. Except, to her, he was the one threatening her…!

Nik stood tall and powerful across the room, his sheer size forbidding. 'Do you want me to go or stay—'

'Stay!'

'Go!'

A humourless smile twisted Nik's mouth as they both answered at the same time. 'As the choice seems to be split down the middle, I think I'll go with the lady and stay. If only to see fair play,' he added with a warning look in Rik's direction.

Rik and Sapphie stared wordlessly at each other, the tension increasing as the seconds passed. She looked so fragile, Rik acknowledged, so vulnerable.

Finally, when Rik didn't think he could stand it a minute longer, Sapphie drew in a deep breath and began to talk. 'Rik, you had no right to come to my home this morning and—'

'I had every right!' he returned, all of his anger seeming to return in a split-second. 'You should have come to me five years ago!'

'And how was I supposed to do that, when it was Dee whom I would have to have asked where you were?' she reminded him. 'I had the same trouble this morning, as it happens,' she added. 'I had to call Jerome.'

'Proving that you could manage to track me down when the incentive was strong enough! You could have done the same thing five years ago if you had wanted to!'

'Asked Dee, you mean?' Sapphie came back.

'If necessary—yes!'

'Just have contacted the woman you were in love with and asked her where I could reach you?'

'Why not?' he returned. 'And I am not in love with Dee!' he added harshly.

'You thought you were five years ago!'

'I thought there was a Santa Claus until I was eight years old; that doesn't make him real!'

'Oh, very funny.' Sapphie glared at him, eyes sparkling deeply amber. 'And when I spoke to Dee, was I also supposed to tell her the reason I needed to reach you was because I was pregnant with your child?'

'Well, it would certainly have been a step in the right direction!' The last thing Rik wanted to do was argue with Sapphie, but at the moment he couldn't seem to help himself.

She drew in a sharp breath. 'You shouldn't have threatened me this morning—'

'What else was I supposed to do—pat you on the head and tell you what a clever girl you are?'

What little colour had stained her cheeks in her anger now quickly drained away, her hands clenching at her sides. 'I'll fight you, Rik. I won't let you take Matthew away from me,' she told him with quiet determination.

'Sapphie,' Rik lowered his voice reasoningly, knowing that shouting at each other wasn't going to help anything. Probably nothing was, but he had to try! 'I'm sure that we can sit down and come to some sort of reasonable compromise that doesn't involve a court battle..'

'That you threatened me with, you mean,' she reminded hardly, her eyes huge pools of accusing amber. 'I don't want Matthew to end up shuttled backwards and forwards across the Atlantic like some sort of human ping-pong ball—'

'You know, Sapphie,' Rik cut in, 'I think we reached the point some time ago in this conversation where what you want isn't of primary importance. Matthew deserves to have a father. Damn it, he has a father—'

'A father he doesn't even know!'

'And whose fault is that, do you think?'

'OK, OK, that's enough.' Nik moved to stand between them as they glared at each other across the width of the fireplace, jaws jutting out aggressively. 'Time out!' he added firmly as neither of them made a move to back down. 'Sapphie, would you please go and sit down in that chair over there?' he prompted gently, giving an approving nod as, after several lengthy seconds, she did so. 'You,' he turned impatiently to Rik, 'sit! And don't give me any arguments, Rik,' he added as Rik would have done just that. 'You're behaving like a child, so I'm treating you like one!'

As if to prove his brother's point, Rik found himself only just managing to clamp his lips shut. He gave a low groan of self-disgust before moving to sit down in the armchair opposite Sapphie's.

He was behaving like a child. In fact, they both were. When it was their son they should have been thinking about, discussing, like the two sensible adults they really were. Nik's was the only voice of reason…

Nik turned to Sapphie, his smile gentle. 'Do you have a photograph of Matthew with you, Sapphie? Of course you do,' he said as she took a small photograph wallet out of her shoulder-bag and shakily handed it to him.

Rik's fingers itched to snatch the wallet out of his brother's hand, to look at his son once again. But the warning look Nik shot him before he began looking at the photographs was enough to advise him against even trying!

Nik's expression was unreadable as he looked at the half-dozen snaps. 'Matthew's adorable, Sapphie,' he told her gruffly as he handed the wallet back before turning once again to Rik. 'He looks just like you did at four years old. It's a pity you had to grow up into an idiot!'

'Now, look—' Rik broke off his protest as Sapphie gave an involuntary laugh, instantly biting her lip as he looked across at her with annoyance.

'Better.' Nik nodded his satisfaction as Sapphie seemed more relaxed. 'Now, I didn't want to stay and listen to this conversation—I was asked to do so. And I'm glad I was. Left to your own devices, you two are just going to rip each other apart.'

He was right. Rik knew that he was. At the moment, he and Sapphie were just continuing to hurt each other.

'Now, I've listened to the two of you,' Nik continued softly. 'And I can see where all the anger and pain is coming from. But in reality there's a very simple answer to this whole problem.'

'Don't tell me.' Rik's mouth twisted derisively. 'We're back to the parable suggesting cutting the baby in two, and the one of us who loves Matthew the most will then back down—'

'Get real, will you, Rik?' his brother interrupted. 'There's absolutely no question about who loves Matthew the most—Sapphie does. She carried him inside her, gave birth to him, has loved and nurtured him for the last four years—Rik, you'll get your chance to talk in a minute, OK? At the moment it's still my turn!' Damn it, Nik always had a way of making him feel five years old!

'This is just a suggestion, you understand?' Nik continued gently.

Nik's suggestions had a way of being orders, but for the moment Rik was willing to give his brother the benefit of the doubt.

'The answer to the problem seems pretty clear to me,' Nik reasoned. 'The answer to all the problems; the lawyers, the tugging Matthew backwards and forwards across the Atlantic, the fact that you're both his parents—'

'Will you just get on with it, Nik?' Rik urged impatiently, having no idea where this conversation was going.

He received another narrow-eyed glare. 'Fine.' Nik nodded tersely. 'Then the obvious answer to all this confusion is for the two of you to marry one other!'

CHAPTER ELEVEN

'AND on that cheery little note,' Nik quipped, as both Sapphie and Rik stared at him in shocked disbelief, 'I will leave the two of you alone together to discuss the possibility!'

Sapphie was barely aware of him leaving the room and closing the door gently behind him.

Marry Rik?

For Matthew's sake, to give him stability rather than subject him to an emotional tug-of-war?

Wasn't it for the very reason that she hadn't wanted to be forced into marrying Rik—or for Rik to feel he had been forced into marrying her!—that she hadn't told him of her pregnancy five years ago?

And yet now, bleak and loveless as it was to her, she couldn't see any other way to resolve this argument...

Hadn't her own mother suggested it as a possibility only an hour or so ago?

And been ridiculed for her trouble, Sapphie acknowledged heavily.

With good reason!

Oh, Rik had made it pretty plain this morning that he wanted her, and she already knew that she loved him—had known that five years ago! But was Rik's desire, and her love, any basis on which to build a happy family life for Matthew? She didn't think so.

Her love for Rik wouldn't fade—it had already been tested to its limits and survived!—but desire certainly could, and probably would.

'It's a ridiculous idea,' she stated flatly; she didn't know what she had expected the outcome of this meeting to be, but it certainly wasn't this!

She didn't look at Rik as she stood up and walked over to the window. As far away from him as was possible in the confines of the Princes' sitting-room!

'Is it?'

Sapphie had been so immersed in her own churning emotions that she hadn't realised Rik had stood up too, that he was only inches behind her. But she could feel his presence now, his heat, the raw pull of his body on hers.

But it wasn't enough!

It would never be enough…

She gritted her teeth, clenching her hands at her sides in order to stop herself from turning and launching herself into his arms; that would solve absolutely nothing!

'Utterly ridiculous,' she confirmed determinedly. 'It would never work.'

Rik's hands came to rest lightly on her shoulders, tightening as Sapphie stiffened at the contact and the fresh assault upon her senses.

'It worked five years ago,' he reminded.

Oh, yes, it had, if Rik was referring—and she was sure that he was—to the explosive passion between them that had held them enthralled from midnight till dawn.

Sapphie had no idea how many times they had

made love, had lost track of time and space, aware only of Rik and the magic of his lips and hands.

Was it any wonder that they had created a child as beautiful as Matthew that night…?

If the two of them married, they could have more children, brothers and sisters for Matthew—

No, she mustn't even go there!

Her shoulders tensed beneath Rik's caressing hands as she dragged herself back from that daydream. 'You're talking about sex, Rik,' she dismissed. 'But even if we could recapture that, sexual attraction fades, and then what are you left with?'

'Liking and respect?' Rik put forward.

She shook her head, shrugging out from under his hands to turn and face him. A move she wasn't sure was a good one as she found herself mere inches away from Rik, his heat enveloping her, even his gaze burning hot as it fixated on her mouth.

Sapphie was almost able to feel, to taste, his lips on hers!

And then, his gaze holding hers now, she really could taste him, as his mouth softly possessed hers as he kissed her, the pent-up emotion inside him spilling out.

How she loved this man!

But how she feared him too, and what he could do to the security of her family!

A sob caught in her throat, caught and held, choking her, the sudden lack of oxygen to her brain making her feel dizzier than ever. This couldn't work, wouldn't work, no matter how many times Rik kissed her in an effort to prove otherwise.

She tried to pull away, but instead found herself held at arm's length as Rik looked at her searchingly. She waited for him to say something, but knew that there really wasn't anything he could say that would make this situation come out right. For any of them.

'OK, Sapphie,' Rik finally sighed. 'Maybe we should forget you and me for the moment and concentrate on Matthew instead.'

She could only stare at him wordlessly, had been expecting more threats, his calm logic taking her completely by surprise.

'Will you at least let me get to know him?' Rik continued softly. 'And allow him to get to know me?'

How could she even begin to stop that happening, if that was what Rik had decided he wanted to do?

She knew that she couldn't, he knew it too, but to give him his due, he was at least giving her the courtesy of asking rather than demanding.

'As what?' she said warily.

'His father, preferably.'

She shook her head. 'That's just going to confuse him.'

Rik's mouth hardened. 'Then, perhaps, get to know me well enough to realise that I'm not the bad man he thinks I am!'

That wasn't too much to ask. In fact, it was nothing really; Rik wasn't a bad man, and if Matthew spent any time in his company he would quickly know that.

'I think that could be arranged,' she accepted slowly.

It was so much more than she had hoped for—in fact, it seemed a little too good to be true!

Rik's hands dropped from her shoulders. 'Then that will have to do as a start. And maybe after we've convinced Matthew we can begin working on convincing you I'm not a bad man, too.'

She had never thought he was a bad man. Not five years ago. And certainly not now. She loved him too much to ever think that of him.

She had no idea whether or not this seemingly impossible situation could ever be resolved, but accepted that they did have to try.

One thing she was certain of; she could not marry Rik as a way of settling the situation. She simply couldn't. Not even for Matthew's sake.

What good would she be doing him when that loveless marriage would inevitably, ultimately, destroy her?

Rik watched Sapphie as the different emotions flickered across her intensely beautiful face, a fist turning in his stomach for what she was going through. She was so tiny and defenceless at this moment that he knew he couldn't take advantage of her fragility. Not when it was his own son that caused that vulnerability!

Sapphie could go, and already had gone, through several kinds of hell because of him, had faced her pregnancy on her own, not even confiding the identity of her baby's father to her family; no, she'd had only her mother's emotional support once Matthew was born, having no father or even stepfather of her own to help her.

She had even lost her job as Jerome's personal assistant because of Dee, and had to find some other way of supporting herself and her child!

He might have been angry with Sapphie earlier, but she had every right to hate him, a man she had believed was in love with her own sister!

What he had once felt for Dee now seemed so shallow and unreal. This woman—Sapphie—was what was real.

He went hollow inside just looking at her, and he couldn't have spoken if his life had depended on it. He admired Sapphie more than anyone else he had ever known, he liked everything about her—and he ached to make love to her again, to show her with his lips and hands how much he...

He what?

Loved her, he knew with startling clarity. He loved Sapphie. Absolutely. Completely.

And she could only look at him with apprehension. Had done so since they met again in Paris.

She was looking at him that way now, too. And he couldn't bear to see that, knew that he had to give her back her sense of security where Matthew was concerned.

'Please don't worry about it any more, Sapphie,' he told her gruffly. 'We can just take each day at a time, see where we go, hm?'

'If you say so,' she answered with that wariness that tore at his insides.

'I do say so,' he assured her. 'Now, how about I drive you home? I'm sure you must want to get back. To Matthew.' He could see the little boy now in his mind's eye, a beautiful child, whom Sapphie loved with all her heart—no matter how she might feel towards his father!

Although Rik could guess at some of what she must feel towards him. Only days ago he had actually accused her of entrapment that night five years ago, of deliberately distracting him because she and her mother wanted Dee to marry Jerome.

What an idiot he'd been!

He still had no idea what had prompted Sapphie to spend that night with him, but he certainly knew it had nothing to do with entrapment. If that really had been the case she would have lost no time, once she discovered she was pregnant, in finding him again.

No, Nik was right, Sapphie really was a lovely lady—in every sense of the word.

Winning the love of a woman like Sapphie was not going to be easy but, loving her as deeply as he realised he did, he was certainly going to try!

'I would like to get back, yes,' Sapphie told him. 'But there's really no need for you to drive me. I came by taxi; I can easily go home the same way.'

'There's every need for me to drive you home,' Rik insisted firmly. 'I— Look, it's the least I can do, Sapphie. Besides,' he added ruefully, 'I don't feel like facing Nik again just yet! Would you?' He grimaced, Sapphie's tremulous smile reward enough for his deliberate self-deprecation.

'He is rather scary, isn't he?' she allowed, her smile less tremulous now.

'Nah,' Rik assured her with a grin. 'Underneath all that arrogance he's pure marshmallow!'

Sapphie looked less than convinced, and still very pale, her eyes huge and troubled.

Rik had taken a step towards her before he was even aware of what he was doing, but her sudden tension was enough to stop him from taking her into his arms again. Instead he lifted a hand and gently caressed one pale cheek. 'I shouldn't have been angry with you earlier,' he told her tenderly. 'I just— It was the shock. But still—' it still was a shock, but one that he was coming to terms with! '—I shouldn't have behaved in the way that I did.'

She looked up at him for several minutes, and then she gave a shake of her head. 'You really don't have to convince me that you aren't a bad man, Rik; I've never thought that you were.'

'Just a misguided one, hm?' he murmured, his gaze roving hungrily over her face; the skin of her cheek was soft and silky to the touch, her hair like living fire as he smoothed several tendrils back from the coolness of her temple.

'Just a misguided one,' she agreed heavily, her gaze no longer meeting his as she stepped away from him. 'Do we have to tell Nik we're leaving or can we just sneak away?' She attempted to be light-hearted.

An attempt that didn't quite come off as her voice shook slightly, but Rik admired her all the more for at least trying.

'Well, as I want to borrow his car to drive you home, I suppose I'll have to tell him.' He fell in with her mood. 'If you hear any shouting, followed by silence, then I'm probably a dead man!'

Sapphie obliged his own attempt at humour with a

smile. Not much of a smile, admittedly, but again, she did try.

It was enough for now, Rik decided.

Although as he walked through the hallway to Nik's study, he knew that he hadn't been completely joking about Nik's reaction; his brother had been a boxing champion in college!

As it was, Nik's ominous silence as he handed over the keys to his car was a lot more telling than anything he might have said; for all of his earlier calm in front of Sapphie, Nik took his role as patriarch of the Prince family very seriously. Matthew was a Prince!

'Not even a black eye!' Sapphie noted when Rik rejoined her in the sitting-room.

'Don't sound so disappointed!'

She eyed him teasingly. 'He's probably just waiting for the appropriate moment!'

'Probably,' Rik said with feeling. 'And it will be when I least expect it!'

Sapphie looked sad again. 'That's how I've felt for the last five years!'

He knew that, could only imagine the extra stress a possible meeting with him must have placed on her already stretched emotions.

'I'm surprised you didn't just hightail it out of Paris last week once you knew I was there.'

'I couldn't,' she replied. 'I didn't dare risk leaving and having either Dee or Jerome saying something to you about my four-year-old son.'

All he ever seemed to have given this woman— besides Matthew—was misery.

Was it any wonder she wanted to keep him at arm's length?

Whereas he just wanted to hold her, and love her, and take care of her. Something he knew she would never let him do!

It was his own fault she hadn't come to him five years ago; how could she have done, in the circumstances?

That knowledge was something he was just going to have to live with. Self-loathing was probably the least of what he deserved for being so utterly stupid.

'I really am sorry, Sapphie,' he said sincerely. 'For everything.'

'I think we both are,' she accepted. 'And there's no going back, so we can only go forward.'

It wasn't what he wanted, and perhaps it never would be, but they had reached some sort of truce. And he certainly wasn't going to give up, was in this for the duration!

Although the spitting virago who confronted him as he opened the car door for Sapphie to get out when they reached her home looked as if she might have other ideas about that!

CHAPTER TWELVE

'DEE...?' Sapphie said, surprised, as she stood by the car and next to Rik and watched as her sister strode forcefully down the pathway, blonde hair flying, her cheeks bright with anger, green eyes glowing like a cat's. 'But I thought you were flying back to the States this afternoon?'

'I was,' Dee confirmed, at the same time moving to stand in front of Sapphie, the full force of her anger directed at Rik as she faced him with all the ferocity of an Amazon warrior. 'Just who do you think you are?' she demanded. 'How dare you come here and threaten my sister in this way?'

Sapphie's initial surprise had turned to complete incredulity now; Dee was here to defend her? That had to be a first. And, given the circumstances, it was very surprising; she would have thought Dee would be angry with her, not Rik.

Dee turned to give her a reassuring smile. 'I was—concerned after your call earlier, so I telephoned the house and spoke to Mummy. She told me what happened this morning, the reason you absolutely had to find Rik.' Dee's mouth tightened as she turned back to face him. 'You may be one of the almighty Prince brothers, Rik, but—'

'Er—Dee—'

'No, Sapphie, I'm not going to shut up,' her sister

second-guessed her. 'You may think that you're all-powerful,' she continued to berate Rik, 'but you'll find I can be just as formidable an adversary if someone threatens my family. Or, at least, Jerome can.'

Sapphie's eyes widened in alarm. 'He isn't here too, is he?' This was already turning into something of a fiasco!

Dee shook her head. 'I persuaded him that it might be better if I came alone. But I'm sure he will be here like a shot if I ask him. You are not going to take Matthew away from Sapphie.' She poked Rik in the chest with one long painted fingernail. 'Not even if I have to give evidence against you myself,' she stated determinedly. 'I don't think a judge would look too favourably on a man who treated Sapphie in the way that you have. I realised long ago, because of the timing, that Matthew's father had to be someone Sapphie met at my wedding. But it never occurred to me that he might be you!' Angry colour had returned to her cheeks and her eyes were glittering with accusation as she stared at Rik.

'Dee, could we go inside and discuss this?' Sapphie suggested. Several of her neighbours were out washing their cars on this lovely summer's afternoon. She was still totally stunned by the fact that Dee was actually here to defend her, and that was without giving the neighbours a free show!

'Fine with me,' Dee acquiesced tightly. 'After you,' she invited Rik challengingly.

To give Rik his due, he looked as bemused by this changed Dee as Sapphie did. Admiringly so? Probably, Sapphie decided. Although, for once, she was sure her little sister wasn't out to impress anyone, that she really was *angry*. Rik was clearly impressed, anyway. She just couldn't win with this man, could she?

'Mummy has taken Matthew to the shops to buy some sweets.' Dee explained Joan and the little boy's absence once they had entered the unusually quiet house. 'I thought it best in the circumstances,' she added, giving Rik another venomous glare. 'You got my sister pregnant, and five years later you think you can just walk back into her life and claim your son? I don't think so!' she snorted.

If Dee had suffered any shock or hurt at this tangible proof of Rik's defection five years ago, then she wasn't showing it; her indignation was all on Sapphie's behalf.

Which Sapphie was still having trouble coming to terms with; what on earth could have happened to bring about this change in Dee? Not that Sapphie was complaining—far from it; it was nice to have her sister as an ally after all these years, rather than an adversary. It was just unexpected.

'There's a lot more to being a father than the act of procreation, you know,' Dee continued her assault.

And Rik continued to take it. Because he was as stunned as Sapphie? Or was it because of that increasing admiration for Dee that Sapphie could see in his eyes?

Sapphie turned away from him, shaking her head. 'Dee, I really don't think…' The pressure of Rik's fingers on her arm silenced her, her gaze questioning as she turned to look up at him once more.

'Let Dee finish what she has to say,' he said softly.

'Take your hands off her!' Dee slapped his hand away from Sapphie's arm. 'Being presented with a lovely four-year-old isn't fatherhood!'

'I do know that, Dee—'

'No, you don't,' she contradicted Rik forcefully. 'Being a father starts way before the babies are even born! It's getting up in the early hours of the morning when your wife is being violently ill with morning sickness. Bathing her face and hands before helping her back to bed. Putting up with her cranky moods. It's holding her hand during the scans, seeing your babies' heads and bodies clearly outlined. And then weeping together when the tests they've taken tell you that they're both healthy—'

'Dee…?' Sapphie looked at her sister wonderingly. 'Their heads and bodies? Both healthy?'

Dee's face softened, tears swimming in her deep green eyes. 'Twins,' she choked proudly. 'And I don't even know them yet.' Her voice strengthened as she turned once again to Rik. 'Haven't held them, kissed them, stroked their creamy cheeks—but I already know that if anyone attempted to take them away from me that I would fight them with every weapon available to me! As I will help Sapphie fight you where Matthew is concerned,' she stated fiercely. 'He's her baby, not yours. He doesn't even know you—'

'Sure he does,' Rik contradicted gruffly. 'I'm the bad man.'

Sapphie felt a knife pierce her own heart at how much that must hurt him. Matthew didn't mean it, of course, he just hadn't liked Rik being angry with his mummy. She would talk that through with Matthew, help him to understand that Mummy had been just as upset and cross.

'I'll talk to him, Rik,' she assured him quietly. 'Help him to understand—'

'How can he possibly understand something like this?' Rik said wearily. 'Dee, everything you've said about me is true,' he continued. 'Except for one thing.' He straightened. 'I will never take Matthew away from Sapphie—'

'Too damned right you won't!' Dee agreed.

'No, Dee—I meant that I won't even try to do that,' Rik explained evenly.

'Oh.' Dee looked taken aback now.

As was Sapphie. She knew that, for Matthew's sake, they had decided to drop hostilities, but she hadn't believed Rik would back down this far... Was it because he didn't want to hurt her and Matthew? Or because of the things Dee had said to him...?

Dee frowned. 'But my mother said—'

'Your mother thought that was my intention when I left here this morning,' Rik explained. 'The—situation has changed since then. I'll leave Sapphie to tell you.' He took his wallet out of his jacket pocket, writing something down on the back of a business card. 'Sapphie, you can call me on this number—any time, day or night—when you have decided I can see Matthew again.' He handed her the card. 'Call me. Soon,' he added, before turning on his heel and striding out of the room, the front door closing softly behind him seconds later.

'Well.' Dee stood like a deflated balloon in the middle of the sitting-room. 'Was it something I said, do you think?' She arched blonde brows.

No matter what he might have just said, Sapphie knew the situation with Rik was pretty bleak, and she still had no idea how it was going to be resolved.

But, at the same time, this change in Dee was so comical she couldn't help laughing. 'You were magnificent!' She hugged her sister before stepping back to look up at her admiringly. 'You had me pretty scared, anyway!'

Dee looked sheepish, then moved to sit down, more shaken by the encounter than she had been willing to show. 'I just hope he never realises that some of that dialogue was a direct steal from a film I made two years ago!' she laughed shakily.

Sapphie's eyes widened. 'Not the bit about the twins?'

'Oh, no, that bit's true,' Dee assured her happily. 'We cancelled our flight after the doctor called us earlier and told us the good news. We were going to come over this evening and tell you over a celebration dinner. Mummy is over the moon!'

'So am I,' Sapphie assured her warmly, relieved—and still slightly surprised!—at her changing relationship with Dee. This was the sort of closeness she had always wanted with her sister. She only hoped it lasted.

Dee looked at her sadly. 'I haven't been a particularly good sister to you so far, have I?' she admitted. 'And I doubt I'm going to change overnight, either. But I am going to try,' she promised. 'For instance,

I'm not even going to ask how you and Rik got together five years ago…!' She gave Sapphie a wry look.

'Best not to,' Sapphie agreed.

Dee smiled. 'It's strange, you know; the twins are here, inside me…' she covered her stomach protectively with her hands '…my bump is hardly showing. And yet I feel different.' Her eyes glowed with sudden laughter. 'I'm probably going to be an atrocious mother, but at this moment in time, now that the morning sickness has finally stopped, and I have my picture of the two of them, I feel as if I could right the world before breakfast and play tennis in the afternoon!'

Sapphie knew that feeling only too well, and, although it abated slightly, it never completely went away.

But, loving Rik as she did, and seeing the admiring way he had looked at Dee such a short time ago, she didn't think it was a feeling she was ever likely to know again…

'Have you been attempting to slit your throat—and failed!—or did you just cut yourself shaving?'

Rik continued to look in the mirror, glaring at his brother's reflection beside his own, his face pulled grotesquely out of shape as he attempted to stick a piece of tissue over the freely flowing cut on his neck.

'Not that I'm complaining either way, you understand,' Nik drawled as he leant against the doorframe to the bathroom. 'All this self-flagellation gets a little wearing after a while, anyway!'

Rik gave his brother a glare, before picking up a piece of fresh tissue and trying again to stop the blood flowing.

'Aren't you overdoing it a little?' Nik continued tauntingly. 'You're only going out for a pizza with Sapphie and Matthew, not off to meet royalty!'

Rik turned after finally succeeding in sticking the tissue to his cut, knowing that Nik was right; the evidence was in the adjoining bedroom—clothes he had tried on and discarded, before settling on faded denims and a white T-shirt. Only to cut himself shaving and bleed all over the T-shirt, meaning he had to start all over again.

Nik and Jinx had very kindly invited him to stay for as long as it took to sort out this situation with Sapphie and Matthew, but, considering this was the first time he had seen either of them since that meeting four days ago, Sapphie having telephoned him yesterday and made the invitation to go for pizza, he had a feeling Nik and Jinx were going to tire of his being here long before any progress was made. In fact, Nik's comment just now confirmed that his brother was already tired of him moping about the place.

Rik sighed. 'This is just so important—I don't know how to explain.'

'You don't need to explain anything to me,' Nik assured him. 'But have you considered that there may be a short cut to all this?'

Rik looked weary. 'I've already told you, Sapphie refuses to marry me!'

'I don't mean that,' his brother returned. 'In the circumstances, I can understand her saying no to that.'

Rik was puzzled; after all, it had been Nik's suggestion in the first place! 'You can?'

'Sure I can,' his brother rejoined. 'Rik, have you tried telling Sapphie that you love her, and then asking her to marry you?'

No, he hadn't told Sapphie he loved her—because he was too wary of what her answer might be!

He had messed this up from the beginning, hadn't appreciated what he had found in Sapphie five years ago; now he was determined to take things at the pace she set. And going out for a pizza with her and Matthew was as good a place as any to start.

The bistro where they were to meet was only a few minutes' walk from where Sapphie lived. However, Rik arrived ten minutes earlier than six-thirty, when Sapphie had suggested they meet, his anxiety to see them again was so acute.

He was sitting at the table drinking iced tea when Sapphie and Matthew walked in the door. His breath caught in his throat at how right they looked together, Matthew holding his mother's hand as the two of them talked and laughed.

Rik wanted to just gather the two of them up in his arms and carry them away to somewhere quiet where he could tell them how much he loved them.

Which would probably frighten the hell out of Matthew—and wouldn't exactly thrill Sapphie, either!

'Hi,' he greeted, standing up as they reached the table, not quite sure whether or not he should kiss

Sapphie and shake Matthew by the hand, or vice versa! Instead he did nothing except smile.

'Matthew,' Sapphie avoided meeting Rik's eyes as she bent down so that she was on a level with the little boy as he looked up curiously at Rik, 'you know we've talked about this, that this is your daddy?'

Rik's breath caught in his throat; whatever he had been expecting, it wasn't this!

If he had thought about it at all—and he had!—he had expected Sapphie to introduce him as 'Rik'; it had never occurred to him that she would have told Matthew—that his son would know—

'Hello, Daddy.' Matthew smiled up at him shyly, still holding tightly to Sapphie's hand.

He swallowed hard, emotion choking him. 'Hello, Matthew,' he finally managed.

Sapphie straightened, obviously not as composed as she appeared as her hands shook slightly, her gaze wary as she met Rik's searching one. 'I thought about what you said,' she said. 'We might as well start the way we mean to go on.'

That seemed practical. Logical, even; there would have been no point in Matthew calling him Rik if he was one day going to call him Daddy. Rik just hadn't expected—wasn't sure he deserved—such generosity on Sapphie's part.

'Thank you,' he accepted, pulling back the chairs for them. 'So, Matthew, what's your favourite pizza?' Not the most inspired of conversation openers, Rik accepted, but it was the best he could do right now, still stunned by the fact that Sapphie had told Matthew exactly who he was.

Actually, the only thing that Rik felt like eating was Sapphie, with his eyes, his mouth, his hands!

She looked wonderful, with her hair swept up in a pony-tail, her make-up minimalised to a light foundation and peach-coloured lip-gloss, her white T-shirt barely reaching the waist of her low-slung denims.

'What have you done to your neck?' Matthew asked a short time later as he wrestled with the trailing melted cheese on his pizza.

Damn, Rik had forgotten all about the tissue on his cut! Which meant he had been sitting here like a moron for the last twenty minutes—Sapphie was obviously too polite to have mentioned it.

In fact, Sapphie was being extremely polite, too polite, when he had hoped the two of them would get to know each other better too.

'An accident while I was shaving,' he explained as he removed the tissue and shoved it in his pocket; Nik could have mentioned it again before he left the house earlier!

'If you had a beard you wouldn't need to shave,' Matthew told him knowingly. 'Uncle Brian has a beard,' he offered, before turning his attention back to his enjoyable struggle with his pizza.

Rik frowned. Uncle Brian? Who the hell was Uncle Brian? As far as he was aware, the only uncle Matthew had was Jerome—he would find out about Nik and Zak later. Much later, as far as Rik was concerned; no doubt Nik had considered it a huge joke earlier to let him leave the house with the tissue still stuck on his neck!

'Brian Glover,' Sapphie offered. 'He's my agent.'

Her agent! Just her agent? Or was there something else between them? Matthew had obviously met the other man…

'Matthew comes with me to see him sometimes,' Sapphie explained at Rik's continued silence. 'When my mother is busy. He's a grandfather four times over, Rik,' she added drily as he just continued to look at her.

Ah. Probably not someone Sapphie would be involved with, then.

But she had already told him that, had said there was no one else in her life but Matthew. And Sapphie, unlike Dee, did not tell him lies. Even if some of her truths he would rather not hear!

Dee had really surprised him that day when he drove Sapphie home, and he had known from Sapphie's stunned expression that, as her younger sister defended her and Matthew with the ferocity of a tigress, she had been surprised too.

Probably it was the first time in her life that Dee had ever taken Sapphie's side in anything! He sincerely hoped it wouldn't be the last, that finally Dee was thinking of someone besides herself. Not that it particularly bothered him what Dee did; she was Jerome's problem—thank goodness!

'That's good,' Rik answered Sapphie's explanation about her agent, just enjoying looking at her.

He never wanted this evening to end, wanted to go right on sitting here, with Sapphie and Matthew, and never leave either of them again. Not that it was going to happen; they were deliberately eating at this early hour so that Sapphie could get Matthew home in time for bed. But it was what he wanted more than he had ever wanted anything before.

'How about dessert?' he suggested once they had finished their pizzas—though Sapphie had merely nibbled around the edges of one slice. 'What do you say, little buddy?' he encouraged Matthew. 'Would you like some ice cream or cake?'

'Chocolate cake, please,' Matthew told him without a moment's hesitation, at the same time giving him a beaming smile.

His son might look exactly like him, Rik acknowledged with a sharp intake of breath, but the rest of him was pure Sapphie. From that unpretentious smile, to his way of saying exactly what was on his mind.

'How about you, Sapphie?' He spoke gently, so full of emotion, of love, that he was surprised he could talk at all.

She smiled teasingly at Matthew. 'I usually have the remains of the chocolate cake that Matthew can't manage!'

Rik already knew from Sapphie that the two of them ate here every couple of weeks or so, and he felt privileged that this time they had invited him to join them; it really was progress, even if it was slower than he would have wished.

'Would you like to come back to the house for coffee?' Sapphie offered as she and Matthew stood waiting while Rik paid the bill—after a slight resistance he had at least won that argument!

Rik looked at her curiously, but her expression was unreadable. Deliberately so? Probably, he conceded;

he had no doubts that this evening was as much of a strain for her as it was for him.

But, Sapphie being Sapphie, he didn't doubt that she was willing to put herself through it for Matthew's sake.

But Rik wanted her to do it for *their* sake, because she wanted to see him again as much as he wanted to see her. It was a lot to hope for, but he could dream, couldn't he…?

'I would like that very much,' he accepted casually, taking one of the boiled sweets out of the basket next to the till and handing it to Matthew. 'There you go, little buddy,' he smiled at his son.

The little boy hesitated about taking it, glancing up uncertainly at his mother. 'Mummy?'

Rik felt something like a knife rip into his chest as he realized Sapphie had probably warned Matthew, as his own mother had him, about never accepting sweets from a stranger. Because, much as it pained him to admit it, that was what he actually was, a stranger to his own son.

Sapphie put a hand on Rik's arm. 'Matthew knows that I don't let him eat sweets in the evening,' she explained softly.

Not because he was a stranger at all! But simply because Matthew knew, and accepted, his mother's rule.

Sapphie smiled down at Matthew. 'But I'm willing to make an exception on this occasion!'

'Yippee!' the little boy cried excitedly before shyly taking the sweet. 'Thank you.' He gave another of those beguiling smiles that almost ripped Rik's heart from his chest.

Because he wanted to give this boy, this woman, the world, if only they would let him; it was a humbling experience to know that Matthew was more than pleased with just a sweet.

'Sorry about that,' Rik apologised once they were in Nik's car and on the short drive to Sapphie's house. 'I guess I'm going to need a bit of guidance on the rules.'

'It doesn't matter.' Sapphie shook her head, reaching up a hand to remove the band from her hair and shake it loose about her shoulders.

Completely taking Rik's breath away for what must be the dozenth time this evening. He wanted more than anything to kiss her, to hold her, to run his hands through that fiery hair. He had felt a need growing all evening, so that now, with her sitting so close to him, the smell of her perfume invading his senses, it was all he could think about, all he—

From the back of the car came the sound of Matthew choking!

CHAPTER THIRTEEN

'STOP the car!' Sapphie screamed as she turned and saw Matthew's face turning blue. 'Rik, stop the…' She didn't finish the second shrill instruction: Rik pulled the vehicle over to the side of the road and jumped out from behind the wheel to pull the back door open.

By the time he had Matthew's seat belt off and had taken him out of the car, Sapphie had joined them. If anything Matthew looked bluer than ever, his eyes wide and frightened as he looked up at her.

Rik didn't hesitate, turning Matthew away from him, putting his arms about the little boy's waist and pulling sharply inwards. A small orange object shot out of Matthew's mouth and he began to cry.

Sapphie gathered the child quickly up into her arms, tears streaming down her face too. 'Oh, God! Oh, God!' seemed to be all she could say, over and over again, as she held Matthew tightly to her, the little boy clinging to her.

'It was that damned candy,' Rik muttered angrily, kicking at the boiled sweet as it lay shattered on the ground. 'I guess Mummy knows best after all, huh, little buddy?' He ruffled Matthew's dark curls as he attempted a weak smile.

Sapphie could see that Rik was really as shaken as

she was by the incident, although she smiled too in an effort to disperse the fright Matthew obviously felt.

'It's OK now, baby,' she told her son huskily.

'I couldn't breathe,' the little boy cried, tears starting afresh.

'Nasty old sweet,' Sapphie declared, before looking up at Rik; his face was as pale as she felt hers must be! 'I'll sit in the back with him for the rest of the journey,' she said.

'Good idea,' Rik agreed, and saw that the two of them were settled in the back seat before getting back into the vehicle himself.

But he kept shooting the two of them anxious looks in the rear-view mirror on the remaining drive home. Sapphie smiled at him reassuringly as she felt the tension leave Matthew and he began to fall asleep.

She never ceased to be amazed at the way children bounced back from things; as a baby, Matthew could be burning up with fever one day and playing happily with his toys the next. Whereas she was usually an emotional wreck from the worry!

It was the same with the sweet, she realised as later they bathed Matthew before putting him to bed; she and Rik were obviously still feeling strained about the whole incident, but Matthew was splashing happily in his bath, completely reassured!

Although not quite…

'Will you be here in the morning when I wake up?' Matthew looked up at Rik with big blue eyes as he lay back in his bed, cosily ensconced under his Thomas the Tank Engine duvet. 'Susie, at kindergarten, she said her daddy is always there in the morning when she wakes up,' he added innocently.

Sapphie swallowed hard as she sat on the side of the bed. In the end she had decided to tell Matthew the truth about Rik because she felt it was best for both of them, even though she had known it was going to make things difficult for her. But she certainly had no idea Matthew had been talking to other children about his daddy at the pre-school he went to three mornings a week.

'Susie's daddy is a teacher, darling,' she explained.

'Oh.' Matthew nodded, obviously not understanding at all. 'What's my daddy?' He turned curiously to Rik.

'I write stories, like Mummy,' Rik answered him carefully, obviously totally besotted with Matthew already.

If he hadn't acted so quickly, hadn't known exactly what to do when Matthew started to choke…!

'Well, Mummy's always here in the morning,' Matthew said happily, as if Rik being here too would be the most natural thing in the world.

And maybe to a four-year-old it was, Sapphie acknowledged ruefully, as they took turns to kiss Matthew goodnight before going down to the kitchen.

To her surprise, Matthew had taken the news that Rik was his daddy with an acceptance that made her proud of him, his only comment being, 'Where did my daddy live before he came to us?' After days of working herself up to telling him, his calm reaction had been a welcome relief, the fact that he had once called Rik a bad man seeming to be forgotten in the excitement of having a father at last.

Sapphie moved about the room making coffee, Rik sitting at the table watching her. Her mother, with her usual tact and consideration, had decided to go to the cinema with a friend this evening. But with Matthew tucked safely in bed, probably already asleep if Sapphie knew him, she and Rik seemed very much alone…

'You're still looking a little pale.' Rik spoke concernedly as she brought the coffee to the table. 'He's OK, you know. And there shouldn't be any side-effects. Should there…?'

'No,' she reassured him, putting the cups down on the table as her hands started to shake as reaction began to set in, having kept herself under tight control in front of Matthew in an effort not to alarm him. 'If you hadn't been there—'

'If I hadn't been there he wouldn't have had the candy in the first place!' Rik put in, standing up to look down at her searchingly. 'But he seemed fine when he went to bed.'

'He is,' Sapphie agreed, tears welling up in her eyes and spilling hotly down her cheeks. 'It's only when something like this happens that you realise how vulnerable they are, how fragile life can be. If anything should ever happen to him—'

'It won't,' Rik told her firmly, clasping the tops of her arms.

Sapphie still shook. 'But if it did—'

'It won't, Sapphie,' he cut in firmly. 'I won't let it!'

She gave a humourless laugh. 'You won't be here to stop it—'

'I'll always be here, Sapphie,' Rik told her forcefully. 'You'll always have me.'

Sapphie became very still, staring up at him, totally bewildered by the intensity of his expression. What did he mean, she would always have him?

Rik gave a deep sigh at her bewilderment. 'Sapphie, I know you aren't ready to hear this, and I really don't want to completely blow any chance I might have of...' He broke off, breathing deeply. 'Sapphie, I love you. I love you!'

She couldn't move, could only continue to stare at him. He didn't really mean that he loved her, she finally decided; it was Matthew he loved, not her. If he was in love with anyone, then it wasn't her—

'You, Sapphie.' He spoke with intensity now, as if he could read her thoughts and was angry at them. 'Only you, Sapphie. It will only ever be you,' he insisted.

'But—but Dee?' she burst out. 'You love her, you've always loved her—'

'I was infatuated with Dee for a while; the fact that she was about to marry someone else intensified that feeling. But what I've remained in love with is another memory of warmth and giving, of fire and laughter.' He spoke as if he had just realised that himself. 'That was you, Sapphie, the night we met. I was all messed up about what I felt, and you and Dee became all mixed up inside my head, but the one I loved was the warm and giving one.'

Sapphie shook her head, afraid to believe him. 'But

I saw your face the day she was here, saw the way you looked at her as she defended my right to Matthew—'

'I do not love her. I have never loved her,' he added with finality. 'What you saw that day was the hope that there was some normal human decency in her, after all,' Rik explained. 'I hadn't seen any evidence of it until that moment! I love you, Sapphie. I always will.'

She looked up at him searchingly, wanting to believe him but was afraid to. She loved him so much that she simply couldn't settle for anything less from him. She wouldn't settle for anything less!

She had to believe him! Rik had never wanted anything in his life as much as he wanted her to believe it was her that he loved!

That he had always loved, he realised now.

That time with Sapphie, happening when he had believed himself in love with Dee, had stopped him from seeing, from acknowledging, that it was the woman he had held in his arms that night that he had continued to love. It had been her warmth and loving that he remembered, that he loved. Sapphie...

She shook her head now. 'You want Matthew—'

'I want you,' he corrected harshly. It was too soon, he knew that, but it was the way the evening had turned out, and he might never have another chance to tell Sapphie how he felt about her. 'I love Matthew, yes,' he acknowledged. 'And if I ever lost him it would half kill me! But if I lost you...! Sapphie, I wouldn't want to go on living without you.' And he knew it was the truth, that Sapphie meant everything to him.

He wanted to be there in the morning when Sapphie woke up, *every* morning for the rest of their lives. But still she said nothing, only continued to look at him warily.

'Sapphie, I want to marry *you*!' He released her, knowing that he couldn't be this close to her and not kiss her. Which wasn't going to help anything at this moment. 'I know, after all that's happened, how difficult it must be for you to believe me,' he groaned. 'I just—I don't know how to explain!' He drew in a shaky breath.

This was just so important, might be the only chance he would ever have to tell Sapphie how he felt. He had to do it right, or risk losing her for ever…!

'When I saw Dee again in Paris, when I first heard her voice, it all came rushing back, all the emotions I thought I had buried long ago. I couldn't breathe, couldn't talk—'

'You love her,' Sapphie stated flatly before turning away.

'I don't even like her!' Rik burst out frustratedly. 'It was you, Sapphie,' he spoke softly as she slowly turned back to face him. 'It was always you…! I just didn't realise it until I saw the two of you together in Paris. Dee is cold, selfish—and incredibly boring,' he admitted. 'You're warm, caring—and I have never known even a moment's boredom in your company.' He gave a rueful smile. 'In fact, the opposite! I can't even think straight when I'm with you.'

Sapphie continued to stare at him. 'That must be very—uncomfortable.'

Rik felt a glimmer of hope as he saw the flicker of amusement in those incredible amber-coloured eyes. Only a glimmer, but it was so much more than he had hoped for.

'No, not uncomfortable at all.' He gave a half-smile. 'Never that. Sapphie, you're the first thought in my mind when I wake up in the morning. All I can think of the entire day. My last thought before I fall asleep at night.' Although he hadn't been able to do much of that this last week! 'In fact,' he added self-derisively, 'Nik assures me that I'm the one who has become boring!'

Sapphie swallowed hard before moistening her lips with the tip of her tongue.

Rik's gaze hungrily followed the movement; he wanted her so much that he just wanted to forget all about caution, his promise to take things slowly, and make love to her here and now. Which would probably ruin everything!

'Nik doesn't know everything.' Sapphie spoke huskily. 'I can assure you, I'm not in the least bored in your company.'

'You aren't?' he breathed uncertainly.

'No.' She looked at him with clear eyes. 'Rik, I haven't been completely honest with you, either.' She swallowed again. 'I— Do you believe in love at first sight?' Her expression was anxious now. Rik frowned his confusion. He wasn't sure he could take listening to her explain her feelings for Jerome—

'You, Rik.' She spoke quietly. 'I'm talking about you,' she explained as he continued to look puzzled.

'Me?' he repeated sharply. 'But I've just tried to tell you that I don't love Dee, that I never loved Dee—'

'Forget Dee,' Sapphie interrupted.

'I would be happy to,' Rik assured her with feeling, wanting to forget that whole embarrassing incident in his life.

'Then it's done.' Sapphie smiled, taking a tentative step towards him. 'Rik, I told you that I was a virgin five years ago. I also told you that I'd had other lovers since. That last part isn't true.'

He could hardly breathe now, staring down at her, needing her so badly, wanting to touch her so badly that he trembled with the emotion.

Sapphie took another step towards him, so close now he could see the brown flecks in the amber of her eyes. 'Rik, I went to Dee and Jerome's wedding believing I was watching the man I loved marry my sister—'

'Don't, Sapphie,' he pleaded huskily. 'I think I can stand anything but hearing how much you love someone else—'

'I said I believed I loved him, Rik.' Sapphie was standing in front of him now, one of her hands reaching up to caress the hard line of his jaw. 'What actually happened that day, when I couldn't bear to even look at the two of them getting married, was that I turned and looked anywhere else instead. And I saw you.' She gave a shaky smile. 'That was when I knew what love was. It was— Rik, I fell in love with you the moment I looked at you. I love you, Rik,' she told him strongly. 'I've always loved you.'

Rik felt as if someone had just punched him, knocking all the air from his lungs. 'You—I—'

'Yes, Rik, you and I,' Sapphie echoed. 'And I don't know about you, but I really don't want to waste another five years of our lives together!' Her eyes glowed with love now.

For him. Only for him. What a fool he had been. What an idiot. He and Sapphie could have been together for the last five years if he hadn't been so blind.

He reached out and pulled her into his arms, crushing her to him. 'I love you, Sapphie! God, how I love you! I never, ever want to be apart from you again!' he promised before his mouth claimed hers in a kiss that left them both breathless and shaking as Rik finally lifted his head to gaze down at her wonderingly. 'Marry me, Sapphie. I think I'll go quietly insane if you don't agree to be my wife!'

She gave a husky laugh. 'I'll marry you, Rik,' she assured him emotionally. 'I'll marry you!' She beamed up at him, her face flushed, her eyes full of love.

It was the way Rik always wanted her to look at him. In fact, he intended doing everything in his power to ensure that she did!

EPILOGUE

'MATTHEW is really into this Santa Claus thing, isn't he?' Rik grinned as he joined Sapphie in the kitchen after going up to say goodnight to their son. 'Not that I'm complaining,' he continued as his arms slid about her waist from behind and he began to nuzzle her neck with warm lips. 'It makes it so much fun for us, too,' he murmured distractedly.

Sapphie turned, almost four months of marriage only having deepened the pleasure she always felt in his arms. 'Makes what so much more fun?' she encouraged laughingly.

'Er—Christmas. I think.' Rik looked down at her with adoring eyes. 'I find it hard to think straight when we're together like this,' he admitted.

The last four months had been the happiest Sapphie had ever known, too, being Rik's wife, being with him all the time, more wonderful than she could ever have imagined. And she knew he felt the same way about her.

Being part of the Prince family really was like being wrapped in warm, protective arms, the four sisters-in-law, Stazy, Jinx, Tyler and Sapphie, having become firm friends. And Matthew absolutely loved his brand-new family, was greatly looking forward to them all spending Christmas together in the Canadian ski resort of Whistler—once they had reassured him that they would leave a note for Santa Claus to tell him where they all were!

Sapphie reached up to kiss Rik lingeringly on the mouth, then she moved away to pick up the two glasses she had filled while he was upstairs, champagne for him and orange juice for her.

'Champagne for me?' Rik murmured appreciatively. 'What are we celebrating?'

'Three things,' she told him glowingly. 'Jerome called while you were upstairs—'

'The twins?' Rik prompted excitedly.

The twins. Not Dee. It had never been Dee, Sapphie knew now with certainty; she and Rik loved each other so completely. And she knew they always would.

'Fergus and Fiona,' she nodded. 'Both six pounds and one ounce,' she announced with a wide, beaming smile. 'Dee is fine. And Jerome sounds over the moon.'

It had continued to be a good pregnancy, Dee's only complaint that she could no longer see her feet by the seventh month!

Her sister hadn't exactly changed overnight, and Sapphie very much doubted that she ever would, but they were closer now than they had ever been as children, and that was more than Sapphie had ever hoped for.

'That's great.' Rik gently chinked his glass against Sapphie's before they both took a sip of their drinks.

'Mm,' Sapphie murmured appreciatively. 'The second thing is that my mother has decided to sell the house.'

'She's decided to move in with us, after all,' Rik said with satisfaction.

Joan had flatly refused to share the new house that Rik and Sapphie bought after their marriage, preferring to stay in the house she and Sapphie had shared after Matthew's birth, claiming the newly-weds needed time together with Matthew as a family, and none of their arguments to the contrary had managed to convince her otherwise.

'Actually…no,' Sapphie grinned, hardly able to contain her excitement. 'She's moving in with Jackson!'

Rik blinked. 'Jinx's father? That Jackson?'

Sapphie couldn't blame him for looking so surprised; she had been a little stunned herself when her mother told her the good news earlier today. Pleased, but definitely stunned.

'Yes, *that* Jackson,' she confirmed happily. 'Apparently the two of them got on so well at our wedding that they've been seeing each other ever since. They didn't tell any of the family, in case things didn't work out. But last night Jackson proposed— and Mummy said yes!'

'Well, I'll be damned…!' Rik exclaimed.

Jinx's father had been widowed a couple of years ago, and Joan had obviously been on her own for many years; Sapphie couldn't have wished for, or imagined, anything more wonderful than her mother falling in love again.

'You said three things…?' Rik reminded softly once they had drunk a toast to Joan and Jackson.

'Oh. Yes.' Colour blazed in Sapphie's cheeks. 'I

know that *No Ordinary Boy* is going into production in the New Year, but could you try and keep the end of July and the beginning of August free?' she prompted shyly.

Rik waggled his eyebrows at her. 'Why, what did you have in mind?'

Sapphie's eyes glowed with love as she looked up at him. 'A quick visit to the hospital before we bring home a brother or a sister for Matthew…!'

Rik went completely still, his face paling, all the teasing leaving his expression as he stared down at her as if he couldn't believe his ears. 'You mean—we're—you're—'

'I'm pregnant, Rik!' she announced excitedly. 'I went to see the doctor this morning when you thought I was out shopping, and—we're going to have a baby,' she breathed huskily, the words catching in her throat.

He swallowed hard, seeming unable to talk, deep blue eyes awash with emotion.

'Isn't it wonderful?' Sapphie smiled, radiant.

'Wonderful! God, I love you, Sapphie,' he groaned as he was finally able to move, gathering her up into his arms and holding her against him with tender possessiveness.

'I love you, too, Rik,' she declared. 'So very much. I always will.'

Always.

It had to be the most wonderful word in the entire English language—

No—that was love.

Something Sapphie had no doubts she and Rik would share for a lifetime…

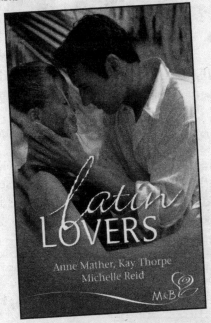

4 FREE

BOOKS AND A SURPRISE GIFT!

We would like to take this opportunity to thank you for reading this Mills & Boon® book by offering you the chance to take FOUR more specially selected titles from the Modern Romance™ series absolutely FREE! We're also making this offer to introduce you to the benefits of the Reader Service™—

- ★ FREE home delivery
- ★ FREE gifts and competitions
- ★ FREE monthly Newsletter
- ★ Exclusive Reader Service offers
- ★ Books available before they're in the shops

Accepting these FREE books and gift places you under no obligation to buy, you may cancel at any time, even after receiving your free shipment. Simply complete your details below and return the entire page to the address below. You don't even need a stamp!

YES! Please send me 4 free Modern Romance books and a surprise gift. I understand that unless you hear from me, I will receive 6 superb new titles every month for just £2.75 each, postage and packing free. I am under no obligation to purchase any books and may cancel my subscription at any time. The free books and gift will be mine to keep in any case.

P6ZED

Ms/Mrs/Miss/Mr ....Initials ....

BLOCK CAPITALS PLEASE

Surname ....

Address ....

....

....Postcode...

Send this whole page to:
UK: FREEPOST CN81, Croydon, CR9 3WZ